Dot, Dot, Dot

Infinity Plus God
Equals Folly

James A. Lindsay, Ph. D.

Dot, Dot, Dot: Infinity Plus God Equals Folly

Copyright © 2013 James A. Lindsay

Published by *Onus Books*

Printed by Lightning Source International

Cover design: James A. Lindsay

Trade paperback ISBN: 978-0-9566948-9-8

OB 04/08

PRAISE FOR *DOT, DOT, DOT: INFINITY PLUS GOD EQUALS FOLLY*:

"A short and engaging read on the meeting of two huge ideas, infinity and God, that leaves us seeing both as abstract ideas that may have nothing to do with reality. Honest and accessible, Dot, Dot, Dot is a great little book to stretch your thinking."

Peter Boghossian, author of *A Manual for Creating Atheists*

"Infinity is not only unbounded in bigness, it is unbounded in weirdness, destroying our intuitions, driving mathematicians to madness, and creating theological nonsense. Fortunately for us, James Lindsay can show the amazing features of the infinite without that many words, and staying very light on the equations. Along the way, he shows how the concept can be misunderstood and abused. Read this to avoid making any more cardinal sins and learn how much math is an amazing human endeavor."

Aaron Adair, PhD, author of *The Star of Bethlehem: A Skeptical View*

"God and infinity have much in common, most notably that they are abstractions conceptually devised by man in order to try to make sense of reality. They are a kind of map. And, as James Lindsay so adeptly points out, we must not confuse the map with reality. For too long (mathematical) Platonic realism has been allowed to underwrite belief in God. With excellent books, like the eminently readable Dot, Dot, Dot, that rug is being firmly pulled from under believers' feet."

Jonathan MS Pearce, author of *The Little Book of Unholy Questions*

Acknowledgements:

The greatest thanks that I owe for the present work is due to my publisher, Jonathan MS Pearce, whom I had approached only for a blurb to accompany an infant version of this book. He decided to take it on as a project of greater scope and weight, and by doing so, he opened the door to reinventing it into something far stronger.

Jonathan was responsible for getting me in contact with the generous Victor Stenger who not only offered to write a foreword for me but offered very sage advice—to rewrite the manuscript from scratch—that may be some of the best that I have been given. For this, Vic deserves and has my lasting gratitude.

Four other people, other than my lovely and patient wife, have my appreciation as well. First, I will mention John W. Loftus for his encouragement, especially with my previous writing. In similar vein, Peter Boghossian has been a great inspiration as well. Next I turn to Richard Carrier for inadvertently challenging me to look deeply into the question of infinity and God. Finally, my friend, who wishes to be identified only by his initials, R.D., was instrumental in helping me explore the mathematical nuances required for this analysis. Thanks to these all.

Contents

• • •

• • •

For everybody.

Foreword

One of the first things students learn in elementary physics is that when a body's position is displaced by an amount Δx in a time interval Δt, then its *average velocity* in that time interval is defined as $\bar{v} = \Delta x / \Delta t$. When they move to Calculus-based physics, they are given the equation:

$$v = \lim_{\Delta t \to 0} \frac{\Delta x}{\Delta t} \equiv \frac{dx}{dt}$$

and are told, or at least given the impression, that this is an exact expression for a measurable physics quantity, namely the *instantaneous velocity* of a body.

It is usually assumed that $\bar{v} = \Delta x / \Delta t$ is an approximation to the "true" velocity, $v = dx/dt$. However, it's the other way around. No one ever measures v. The best they can do is measure $\Delta x / \Delta t$ in as small a time interval Δt as possible.

If they make it to graduate school, students may get wind of the fact that the uncertainty principle of quantum mechanics along with the notion of black holes limits the smallest measurable distance to the *Planck length,* 1.616×10^{-35} meter and the smallest measurable time to the *Planck time,* 5.391×10^{-44} second. Thus we can never measure even in principle an instantaneous velocity. The unmeasurable $v = dx/dt$ is just an approximation to the measurable $\bar{v} = \Delta x / \Delta t$ for small time intervals.

Since the Planck length and time are so small compared to what we are capable of measuring, until we get to the cosmology of the early universe, we can

1

get away with treating space and time as continuous and use Calculus to make accurate predictions about the observed motion of bodies.

If the velocity of a body is not constant but varies with time in a specified way given by a function $v(t)$, students are taught they can calculate the distance the body travels in a time t as

$$x = \int_0^t v(t)\,dt = \lim_{n \to \infty} \sum_{i=1}^n v(t_i)\Delta t_i$$

where the time interval from 0 to t is divided up into n segments Δt_i.

Here the symbol "∞" is called *infinity*. Let's see what it means. We usually think of the sum as an approximation to the area under the curve of $v(t)$ vs. t. The smaller Δt_i or the larger n, the more accurate is the approximation. The "exact" result is obtained by putting in the functional form of $v(t)$ inside the integral and instead of actually doing a laborious sum, by calculating the integral using the rules of Calculus. These rules apply for the case where $n = \infty$, which physics students, at least, picture as the largest possible number.

But what is the value of infinity? As mathematician James Lindsay points out in this unique and fascinating book, no matter how large a number we can think of, we can always add one to it, or double it, to make it larger. In fact, infinity is not a number at all.

Thanks to the brilliant work of Georg Cantor (1845-1919) and others that followed, notably David Hilbert (1862-1943), mathematicians now have a good grip on a precise theory of infinity. Lindsay does not get into

2

the technical details, but provides an entertaining discussion of the many weird and counterintuitive implications of this strange object called infinity.

For example, we are accustomed to thinking of numbers such as 1, 7, and 13 as "small" and numbers such as one thousand, one billion, 10^{100}, or the *googolplex*, which is 1 followed by 10^{100}, zeros as "large." (Guess where "Google" came from). But, Lindsay points out, even these latter numbers are "embarrassingly small" since there are far more numbers, indeed, an unlimited number of numbers, that are larger than any of them.

Most scientists and mathematicians use the world "infinity" when they really mean unlimited or unbounded. Or sometimes just "very large." Lindsay has no problem with that and notes that it is a common colloquialism that we are not going to change. However, it is important not to forget that there is no such number infinity, especially when we start thinking about using it ontologically.

Throughout the book, Lindsay discusses how theologians attempt to relate infinity to God. In particular, he refers to the numerous writings of the evangelical Christian apologist William Lane Craig, who is famous for his debates with atheistic scientists (including two with me). Craig is well versed in mathematics and cosmology and for years has promoted what he calls the *Kalām Cosmological Argument* for the existence of a creator. This argument is based on the theorem published in 1970 by Stephen Hawking and Roger Penrose that showed the universe had to begin as a singularity, a point of infinitesimal size and infinite density. (The infinitesimal is another non-number treated as a number that can be thought of as $1/\infty$).

3

Craig originally used the cosmological singularity to argue that time itself began at that point, thus "proving" that not only our universe but everything that is had a beginning at that time. He then proceeded to claim, on no basis, that anything that begins must have a cause and, in the case of the universe, that cause is the personal God of Christianity.

However, the Hawking-Penrose theorem was based on Einstein's theory of general relativity and, as both authors admitted almost thirty years ago, it is not a quantum theory and so does not apply to the origin of the universe.

Furthermore, since that original work cosmologists have found good reasons to consider that our universe may be just one of many in what is termed the multiverse. While this profound notion is far from proven, we must keep its prospect in mind. In what follows, I will use "multiverse" to refer to everything that is, which should be taken as allowing but not requiring other universes beside our own.

In his later writings, Craig seems to have implicitly recognized that the singularity did not happen after all and he accepted the possibility of a multiverse. So he has come up with argument for why the multiverse must have had a beginning and thus a creator. If the multiverse were eternal, according to Craig, then it would have begun an infinite time ago, in which case we would never have reached the present.

In 1925, Hilbert gave a speech in which he said, "The infinite is nowhere to be found in reality. It neither exists in nature nor provides a legitimate basis for rational thought." I assume that by "reality" he was referring to the phenomena we observe in the world with our eyes and scientific instruments. Also, I am not sure what he meant about infinity not being a basis for rational thought. Surely his and Cantor's work on the concept of infinity was rational.

In any case, Craig quotes Hilbert to bolster his argument for a beginning to the multiverse. If there is no actual infinity, according to Craig, then the multiverse cannot be eternal, that is, it could not have begun an infinite time ago.

However, an eternal multiverse would not have had a beginning an infinite time ago. It would have had no beginning. Running a clock backwards and counting the ticks: -1, -2, -3, . . ., we never get to -∞. The time from now to any moment in the past is a finite number of ticks.

Here Craig, as is often the case for apologists, tries to have his cake and eat it too. As we have seen, first he tried (unsuccessfully) to use the Hawking-Penrose infinite singularity to prove time and everything else that exists had a beginning. Then he tried (unsuccessfully) to use Hilbert's statement that no infinities exist in reality to argue that the multiverse cannot be eternal. Next he joined other theologians in attributing infinite capacities, including eternity, to deity. This is an example of what Hilbert may have been thinking when he said that infinity provides no legitimate basis for rational thought.

Many prominent contemporary mathematicians and theoretical physicists seem to disagree with Hilbert about the nature of reality. Mathematician Penrose has explicitly admitted that he is a Platonist who views the abstractions of mathematics as the underlying reality of perfect forms envisaged by Plato. Infinity is one of these abstractions. Modern quantum field theorists similarly view the fields in their theories, which contain infinities, as the "true reality" while the particles that experimental particle physicists register in their detectors are the shadows on the wall of Plato's cave.

In an article in the December 2012 *Scientific American*, Cambridge theoretical physicist David Tong wrote: "Physicists routinely teach that the building blocks of nature are discrete particles such as the electron or quark. That is a lie. The building blocks of our theories are not particles but fields: continuous, fluidlike objects spread throughout space."

In physics, a strong connection exists between measurement and theory. Quantities that are not actually measurable are represented in theoretical models by abstract mathematical objects. Many theoretical physicists follow Plato and Penrose in taking these abstractions to be elements of an objective reality that lies beyond what is measured. Thus, while distances less than the Planck length and times less than the Planck time cannot be measured, a space-time continuum nevertheless exists "in reality." The time t is then not just a count of ticks on a clock, always a rational number when converted to seconds or other time units, but an irrational number with in infinite number of decimal places.

In *Dot, Dot, Dot*, mathematician Lindsay makes a clear distinction between the abstractions such as infinities, infinitesimals, and continua used in mathematical and theoretical physics, and what is measured in the laboratory. Quantum fields are such abstractions. No one has ever observed a quantum field. Furthermore, there is simply no way we can know what is ultimately real. All we know about the world is what we observe.

Quantum field theory and all the other wonderful abstractions of mathematical physics are rational, not to mention useful. Where would we be without complex numbers? These abstractions enable us to make accurate predictions of observed phenomena. But they, like God, are just human inventions.

Victor J. Stenger
15th September 2013

Victor J. Stenger is emeritus professor of physics and astronomy at the University of Hawaii and adjunct professor of philosophy at the University of Colorado. He is author of the 2007 *New York Times* bestseller *God: The Failed Hypothesis* and eleven other books including *The Fallacy of Fine-Tuning* and *God and the Folly of Faith*.

Dot, Dot, Dot

Introduction

For some time, the mathematical concept of the infinite—that which is limitless and impossible to count—has been tied up with the mythological concept called "God." I don't claim to know why this is the case. In the past, I have suggested that perhaps it is a result of an arms race between memes.[1] Perhaps this happened specifically because religions, as their influences spread, had to account for the beliefs of neighboring peoples. Bigger gods can be more inclusive, after all. Perhaps it also occurred out of simple, immature desperation to pump up certain unprovable claims. Perhaps it is both. At any rate, those who argue for the existence of God seem drawn to the notion of the infinite, not unlike a moth to a flame. This metaphor is telling. Indeed, the more I have thought about it, the more I have come to realize that the subtitle of this collection offers a reasonable word of caution: infinity plus God equals folly.

I say so because a wide majority of arguments, both for and against belief in God, that call upon infinity are deeply problematic. It is probably not controversial in the least to point out that this fact may rest heavily upon a simple reality: math is hard. Most people just don't know enough mathematics to talk competently about infinity. It is probably slightly more controversial to suggest that it is also because most of the people who wish to argue on behalf of God in this way subscribe to an underlying philosophy,

---

[1] In my *God Doesn't; We Do: Only Humans Can Solve Human Challenges* (2012), CreateSpace Independent Publishing Platform, p. 67.

including about mathematics, which complicates matters and may defy the evidence.

Infinity is wrapped right up in the concept of God, and it probably cannot be extracted from the ideas that form the basis for contemporary theism. Indeed, that the infinite is bound up with God is even a Catholic dogma. The entry for infinity in the *Catholic Encyclopedia* says this explicitly: "The actual infinity of God in every respect is Catholic dogma," it reads.[2] Whatever the reasons may have been that led infinity to be tied to God, in light of its status as dogma "in every respect," it would be fair to say that the bond is permanent and defining. It is my view that this unification of the divine and the infinite presents an insurmountable problem for theology.

My list of goals then, with publishing this book, based upon what was originally a collection of essays, is headed with the idea that people who wish to use infinity in theological or philosophical arguments usually need to take a great deal more care in doing so lest they burn themselves. It isn't far off the mark to say that we simply cannot see infinity, so the very idea carries with it a real sense of impenetrable philosophical darkness that we tuck away neatly within the three dots—known as ellipsis—that gave the title to this book.

To help readers follow the necessary material, the first part of the book endeavors to offer some modest amount of clarity of this extremely opaque, obscure, even arcane, topic. In fact, I'm also including a glos-

---

[2]   Zimmerman, Otto. "Infinity." *The Catholic Encyclopedia.* Vol. 8. New York: Robert Appleton Company, 1910. 18 Sept. 2013.

sary of mathematical terms at the end to help readers bridge the gap to this technical language, along with a list of recommended reading for more information.

Other goals I have set out to achieve include helping people to see the philosophical foundations of mathematics differently than they may already. Though there are several positions that can be held in that regard, I specifically want to forward my own understanding, which lies between two positions called "intuitionism" and "formalism," informed by "fictionalism." Particularly, I favor these over "Platonism." Platonism holds that abstractions have meaningful reality in their own realm known as the "realm of ideals," independent of minds to think them, and Platonism is relevant because it leaves us confused between the abstract and the real.

I do not accept the Platonist position. Specifically, I feel that the realm of ideals at the center of Platonism is really an attempt to give abstractions a sense of reality, which is to say to reify them. In short, then, I think mathematical and other Platonists are reading too much into their own ideas. Another important point in this vein, though, is that Christianity and many other theistic religions are based specifically upon variants of Platonism. These religions see "God" as an extant being, one not always limited to exist within a perfected realm of ideals. Indeed, they give it some metaphysical or "spiritual" reality. I see "God" simply as a variety of abstract concepts. The key difference is that abstract concepts do not—cannot—interact with the world as an agent. In an important sense, then, I see drawing a distinction between theology and mythology as little more than confusion about whether or not abstract concepts have meaningful reality, at least in one light.

11

Mathematics provides a model of the world that we employ for our understanding of it, and this model shouldn't be confused with the reality it helps us to understand. This also happens to be a substantial part of how I view the idea of "God" now as well. I think of each idea of "God" as an informal, very poorly defined abstraction, and I see belief in God as a way to try to make sense of the world by means of a reification of the "God" abstraction.

To elaborate a little on these terms here, my feelings about the philosophical foundations of mathematics are that mathematical ideas are formal and abstract constructions, perhaps even little more than useful fictions, and mathematics is what emerges from examining them through various lenses we call logics—yes, plural. My experience in mathematics, in which I hold a doctoral degree, leads me toward this view, and I extend that thinking to abstract notions in the broader world, including science and, critically, theology.

In contrast, mathematical Platonists, following Plato's philosophy, give meaningful "reality" to abstractions, some even believing that they constitute the true underlying nature of reality. Plato spoke about a "realm of ideals" in which the perfect "forms" of all things exist with everything in the real world being merely shadows of the ideal forms. For me, the problem is that this realm itself doesn't "exist" in the same way that, say, mountains and tables exist. Mental stuff depends upon, and "exists" only in minds.

The Platonic view isn't entirely absent in modern mathematics. As mathematician Ian Stewart put it in his *Letters to a Young Mathematician*, "the working philosophy of most mathematicians is mostly an unexamined Platonist-Formalist hybrid"[3] (p. 26). I feel there are decent, seductive, and ultimately misleading reasons that mathematicians—especially those who haven't carefully examined their foundations—would accept some degree of Platonism, and those reasons will hopefully be made bare throughout this book.

A close look at Platonism makes it feel a little odd, though. In it, broadly speaking, there are concrete ideals in the realm of ideals: the ideal imagined form of a chair, for instance, which motivates the construction of the real chair. But notice how vague this is; chairs come in many shapes, and when exactly would the ideal form of a chair become that of a loveseat or a couch instead? More importantly, there are also abstract ideals like liberty and justice—and numbers—that cannot be tied to physical objects.

At the pinnacle of the ideals is "The One," the ideal of goodness. Described by Neoplatonists, The One is "the primeval Source of Being," also known as "the Infinite," said to be "the source of all life, and therefore absolute causality and the only real existence."[4] This abstraction is the philosophical underpinning of the Christian God, elevated from Yahweh, battle god of the desert, and thus the entire God-concept embraced by the largest religious positions in the world. Infinity is tied up in this ideal, perhaps inextricably, and it is my informed opinion on the matter that this is folly.

---

[3]   Stewart, Ian (2006), *Letters to a Young Mathematician (Art of Mentoring)*, New York: Basic Books, p. 26.

[4]   From the *Wikipedia* entry for "Neolatonism," subsection "The One." http://en.wikipedia.org/wiki/Neo-Platonism#The_One (accessed 19 Sept. 2013).

The present work was written originally as a variety of essays centered upon this huge topic, and it has not been my intention to be comprehensive! In fact, it is quite the opposite; as I want only to illustrate a few points and open the door to discussion, I aimed for brevity in place of completeness. Of particular note, this work is not intended primarily as a unified treatment of the topic of infinity, even as it applies to the discussion about the meaning and existence of "God."

Many of the chapters here were once essays derived from similar ones on my blog, which is named *God Doesn't; We Do* after my first book. All of those have been edited, sometimes heavily, for their inclusion in this book. It is my hope that you enjoy it, and I hope if nothing else that it gets you to raise an eyebrow a little at any theological or philosophical argument involving the idea of infinity—even my own.

James A. Lindsay, June 2013

• • •
Getting Acquainted
• • •

Mathematics is a subject with a rather severe barrier to entry. In fact, it is common for mathematicians to struggle in their personal lives with the fact that it is almost impossible to have a normal conversation about their work with almost anyone—which is surprisingly lonely at times. While many fields of study allow students and even lay people somewhat clear glimpses into the research frontier, in mathematics, the view is completely opaque. Calculus, often considered "the highest math" by college undergraduates, is five hundred years old. Doctoral-level students in mathematics only occasionally touch upon topics in their coursework that is newer than fifty or sixty years old, the bulk having been done almost a century (or more) ago. Only in their specialized fields of research do top-level students of mathematics typically press forward toward the current research frontier. In science and technology, this would be death, but formal mathematics simply doesn't change once established. Once the axioms at the foundations are agreed upon, a mathematical proof is in a sense a timeless thing—and there's a reason for this near the heart of my purposes. Still, because of the distance between the laity and the mathematician, it is useful here to spend a few pages getting acquainted with these ideas and where I intend to go with them.

Dot, Dot, Dot

1

A Story About Infinity

Here I hope specifically to try and bridge the gap, which is frequently broad, between lay knowledge and some of the precise mathematical terminology that I use in this book. This is no easy task, particularly since I don't want the tone to come off like reading a dictionary of dull, technical terms. Instead, here I want to set the overarching tones of the collection, which is to say first that infinity and God are incompatible and second that I lean away from Platonism as a philosophical foundation of mathematics and, by extension, mature philosophy of all kinds.

. . .

In the beginning, there were things, and there were no people to count them. After a time, there were people who could benefit by counting those things. Thus, the people abstracted and invented numbers so that they might count the things. Whether the people realized it or not, the numbers they counted with were not the things themselves, and neither did those numbers exist independently as things in themselves. Though the numbers of the things they had to count were frequently quite limited, the people realized that it is conceptually possible to have more things. Adding another thing therefore seemed, in principle, like something that could be done at any time, if only another thing were to be had, and so they abstracted again. They created the concept of a successor, the abstract idea of a next counting number, though many centuries lay between its conception and its formal description. The people had already abstracted far enough to have divorced the concept of number from the objects thereby enumerated, and so numbers took on an existence of their own—an abstract, nonphysical existence. Numbers could be applied to any sort of objects; they were useful; and it was good.

A problem exists at the heart of this simple story, an accurate enough myth to describe the birth of systems of enumeration. That problem is that numbers, as abstract objects of their own kind, which is to say as mental objects, are not constrained by questions about physical reality. On the face of it, this is hardly a problem set against their utility; it holds no effective weight against counting. But when the unfettered abstract notion of "number" is combined with the unhindered abstract concept of successorship, a very hard question naturally arises, spawning a concept that is often used and misused and that appears to be paradoxical to the core. This concept is infinity, the boundlessness that captures the idea that we know that no counting number can accurately be called the largest. As abstractions, they do not depend on actual things to count and thus all have a successor that is larger.

Dealing with this issue requires us to be quite formal in our treatment of mathematics, a rather new invention given how long we've been counting things. The first real formalization that I want to discuss is alluded to just above: the set of fundamental assumptions called the Peano Axioms that define our theory of numbers. These are named for Italian mathematician Giuseppe Peano, who devised them in the late nineteenth and early twentieth centuries. My intention will be to keep this part brief and light, but some introduction of terms is clearly going to be necessary. In fact, we need to start by understanding the term *axiom*.

Axioms are statements that are taken to have been accepted to be self-evidently true as starting places for our reasoning. In other words, these are statements for which no proof is given, not least because they are the statements upon which proofs will be constructed. Yet another way to put this is that axioms are the statements upon which abstractly defined structures are based. It is fair to say that axioms, in fact, are the presumptions that allow us to reason logically about matters of interest to us in the first place. Because they are presumptions, it is generally accepted (as rule of thumb) that parsimony, meaning the acceptance of as few assumptions as are absolutely necessary, is desirable in constructing *axiomatic systems*—abstract structures arising from applying logic to the axioms.

That axioms are exempted from proof is a matter that is easily and frequently taken out of context, often applying the term "faith" inappropriately when doing so. Axioms are, again, statements that are accepted to be self-evidently true, which is a long way from being statements that are simply dreamed up. We exert judgment on the worth of an axiom by the degree that we might consider it self-evidently true. Sometimes we have good insight here; sometimes we must consider these matters carefully based upon the resulting framework of truths that emerge from the axioms themselves. These frameworks, called axiomatic systems, are the only places where we have proofs of mathematical or philosophical certainty. Thus, the kind of certainty we call "mathematical" is always held in relationship to a collection of underlying axioms.

19

An example that is quite famous in this regard is that of the "parallel postulate" of Euclidean geometry, often expressed in terms of slightly the stronger statement called Playfair's Axiom: *Given a line and a point not on it, at most one parallel to the given line can be drawn through the point.* This axiom, along with the other axioms of geometry, define Euclidean (flat space) geometry, the kind most of us learn about first as children. Playfair's Axiom does not hold for curved spaces, though, and so using it as a fundamental axiom of geometry restricts us from being able to develop geometric systems for curved spaces—a major hindrance. Flat spaces may seem self-evident, particularly in Euclid's day, some 2300 years ago, but we actually have need of geometry that deals with curved space in reality. Thus, giving them self-evidential status cannot hold. We have a choice, then, of accepting the axiom to derive truths that apply only to flat spaces, which is extremely useful for practical application as well as for simplicity's sake, or rejecting it and having to deal with a broader logical framework for geometry. Often, we do both and simply specify which paradigm we are working within.

Axioms, then, are presumed and can be chosen or rejected, and yet they are hardly arbitrary. When they do a poor job of matching with reality or preclude us from having the abstract toolkit we need to work with reality, we develop other axiomatic systems to account for the situation. Mathematics and philosophy, then, far from being monolithic structures, are based upon diverse collections of various axiomatic frameworks developed and chosen for their utilities. The number theory mentioned at the beginning (in mythological language) is one such example: the Peano Axioms can be used to lay out the foundations of number theory, by which objects can be enumerated whether they exist or not.

. The concept that each number defined by the Peano Axioms has a successor is itself part of the Peano Axioms. This idea seems very natural and self-evident: it essentially states that however many things we have, we can conceive of the idea of adding another, even if we were to know that in the physical universe there isn't another thing to add. Of course, considering the previous sentence, we could digress into endless and mostly fruitless postmodern discussions about what "self-evident" really means if in reality we couldn't add another thing even if we wanted, but we needn't do that. In principle, the notion of "always another" hardly offends our better sense, and in the abstract, there's no limitation that would prevent it. This idea presents an issue, though.

The issue is that we cannot say that the numbers ever stop, even if there are no physical objects to count with them. No matter the value we have at hand, by the Peano Axioms there is another number larger than it called its successor. The resulting concept of limitlessness is itself an abstraction, the abstract notion of being without limit in quantity, and we call that concept "infinite," superficially meaning "not finite." Abstractly, this seems to make some sense, but physically, it may or may not. Already, then, we find an idea, defined by yet another axiom, we can hardly call "self-evident," making these matters tricky.

As an aside, note that some religious apologists, notably Christian apologist William Lane Craig, are fond of trying to adhere to this conception of infinity as a quality of unboundedness, not a quantity, however inextricably the notion of quantity is tied to infinity. In doing so, Craig is in some surprisingly good company.

Archimedes rejected the notion of infinity being a quantity, stating that infinite collections of things do not exist, and antitheistic philosopher and historian Richard Carrier, who attacks Craig's work rather sharply and effectively, also claims the Archimedean principle that there are no "actual" infinities, meaning infinite quantities instead of the unbounded potential for more. A relatively small branch of mathematicians, called either finitists or ultrafinitists, also hold this view. Most mathematicians, though, tend not to think of infinity so concretely at all. Abstractions can be abstract.

As it turns out, the Peano Axioms can also be used to allow us to develop a way of describing collections of objects, such descriptions being known in mathematics as "set theories." The collections of objects (usually abstract objects) are in many cases known as sets. The question about whether or not there is an infinite set, like the set of all of the counting numbers, immediately arises from the Peano Axioms, but as it turns out, the Peano Axioms do not equip us to be able to answer this question! This fact was not known for a long time, during which these matters presented some major challenges to mathematicians. People abstracted again, though, and an axiom, called the axiom of infinity, was proposed. This axiom directly leads to the idea that there exists at least one infinite set, an "actual" infinity. As I will elaborate upon later, the Peano Axioms seem to predict this axiom, and yet the set theory they produce refutes it.

In the late nineteenth century, mostly driven by limitations arising in analysis (the theoretical foundations of calculus) this question about whether or not to accept the axiom of infinity came to a head. One mathematician, Georg Cantor, who is now famous for it, was able to work with the notion of infinity in a new and coherent way. Highly controversial at the time, needing several decades and the endorsement of mathematical heavyweight David Hilbert (a committed mathematical formalist) to gain some measure of acceptance, Cantor's ideas laid the groundwork that quantified infinity. As a result, it also gave mathematicians the toolkit, via a complete reformulation of set theory by Ernst Zermelo and Abraham Fraenkel, to solve many of the long-standing problems in mathematical analysis. It is on this basis that the majority of mathematicians today accept the Zermelo-Fraenkel Axioms of set theory (with yet another additional axiom added to it; see below). To be clear, the Zermelo-Fraenkel Axioms explicitly include the axiom of infinity.

Putting firm, if abstract, footing under the quantitative nature of infinity bore many consequences. Among these, one of the most famous is that infinity is not a one-size-fits-all concept, a question over which there was much contention, some of it quite bitter, before Cantor's work was accepted. Cantor was able to show that if we postulate at least one infinite set, then we necessarily get more sizes of infinity. For instance, the infinity that describes the size of the natural numbers is smaller than the infinity that describes the size of the real numbers. Indeed, he showed that given any infinite set, it is possible to create an infinite set that is properly larger. The immediate consequence here, as with the successorship property of numbers, is that if we have one size of infinity, then we have infinitely many sizes of infinity. It was later shown that the infinity that tells us the size of the counting numbers is the smallest infinity and, slightly ironically and yet meaningfully, this size is known as *countable*

23

infinity. All other, larger sizes of infinity are collectively known as *uncountable* infinities.

Astute readers will, at this point, recognize a question raised by the fact that there are infinitely many infinities: which one tells us how many infinities there are? Stunningly, the answer is that we can't know without making additional assumptions beyond even those of Zermelo-Fraenkel! This fact comes to us from another famous name, Kurt Gödel, who was able to prove in 1940 that given any axiomatic system that can produce arithmetic, we have to choose between completeness and coherence. Completeness means that the truth value of every statement in the system is determinable—that is that all statements can be assigned the appropriate truth value (usually true or false, for us). Coherence means that there are no contradictory statements, which is to say no paradoxes, within the system. We can have one or the other, but except in very special cases that have little applicability, we cannot have both.

Cantor's work in the 1870s motivated Gödel's, which itself wasn't even completed in this regard until Paul Cohen put it together in 1963, so for many decades these ideas were highly contentious because, not only did we not know the answers to some apparently fundamental questions, we didn't know that we couldn't know. In the intervening time, a lot of diligent work was done pursuing various avenues related to the field, and a very important concept was determined to be intimately related to the question at the center of the sizes-of-infinity controversy. This important concept is known as the *axiom of choice,* which needs its own elaboration.

The axiom of choice states that if we have an infinite collection of sets of indistinguishable objects, each containing at least one object, then we can choose exactly one object from each set. As a quick reminder that grossly oversimplifies, a *set* in mathematics can be understood to be a collection of objects, usually abstract objects. A very loose way to conceive of the idea of the axiom of choice is to imagine we have an infinite number of drawers, each containing any nonzero number of indistinguishable balls. The axiom says that we are able to make a collection of balls by choosing exactly one ball from every drawer.

On the surface, this seems uncontroversial, perhaps because for the majority of the examples we might think of at first, there is some selection scheme. Using sets of whole numbers, we might select the smallest value; using balls, we might imagine taking the ball closest to the front, left corner of the drawer. The problem doesn't exist in those cases, though, and so that's not what the axiom refers to. The problem arises when we do not have a selection criterion. In the example, the balls are all taken to be indistinguishable so as to give the idea that we've eliminated the possibility of a *choice function* that would tell us how to choose each ball from its drawer. Since there are infinitely many drawers and no specified collection mechanism, how could we be sure that we are able to choose some specific infinite collection of balls? We cannot go through each drawer one-by-one because we'll never finish, and we can't draw them all out "at once" because we don't have a scheme by which to do it. As it turns out, we need an axiom that says we can do it, essentially because we say so.

This axiom was considered to be highly controversial until quite recently, when most mathematicians gradually started to accept it because it allows us to produce useful mathematical results. It does have some uncomfortable consequences, however, that we'll discuss later. This matter was settled recently enough so that it is still somewhat common to hear today's mathematicians explicitly point out when they are using the axiom of choice.

When the axiom of choice is added to the Zermelo-Fraenkel Axioms of set theory, the resulting framework, abbreviated ZFC for "Zermelo-Fraenkel plus Choice," provides the context for modern mathematical set theory and is the predominantly accepted axiomatic mathematical framework. It goes far beyond the scope of my intentions here to get into this particular topic much more deeply, save the need to introduce a few more terms. For most of my purposes, then, the story of infinity is essentially told.

I would like to point out, however, the very humanness of all of this, since my ultimate purpose here is to discuss how these ideas relate to other conceptions called "God," other ideas utterly covered in human fingerprints. A point that is illustrated to some degree here is that, regardless of what Platonists want to believe about ideals, realms of forms, and the underlying nature of reality, a very strong case can be made that human beings are the ones fashioning logic and logical axiomatic systems as mental tools through which we aim to better understand our world. On some level, Platonists believe just the opposite—that abstractions determine a fundamental reality and that we are merely discovering those "real" abstractions as we go along.

Instead of getting into those weeds now, here we find an excellent place to recap where we have already been and a moment to reinforce this new terminology—hopefully without making it any more complex than it already is (because this rabbit hole goes deep and gets weird). We started only with the need to count things. Then we noticed that because in principle, even if not in practice, we can always add another thing, we abstracted the idea of successorship. Both of these ideas, numbers along with successorship, taken as abstractions upon reality, led us to formalize ideas known as the Peano Axioms, which predict but deny the axiom of infinity (when applied to set theory). A reformulation, known as the Zermelo-Fraenkel (ZF) Axioms of set theory, accepts the axiom of infinity and thereby lets us answer many questions, although other questions lurk at the heart of what arises—not least what an infinite tower of infinities could possibly mean. Of particular note, the axiom of choice that allows us to select from infinitely many nonempty bins is generally accepted, only lately, as a foundational part of set theoretic mathematics, and the resulting framework is abbreviated ZFC. And we have all of this because we recognized that our little-old counting numbers are abstractions in the first place.

Dot, Dot, Dot

2

The Map and the Terrain

A recurring theme that I encounter from religious apologists is their strong tendency to try to argue God into existence via any number of claims to necessity. What sticks out to me, though, is that they *always* resort to philosophical-style arguments instead of being able to present verifiable evidence for the existence of their God (among other theological claims). This is truly bizarre. It would seem likely, then, that apologists at least partially confuse the map for the terrain, to make a useful analogy, possibly because they (especially Christian apologists) lean so heavily upon Platonic thinking.

. . .

Cogito ergo sum, right?

A chief goal of religious apologists and, indeed, any philosopher who plays in the philosophical field of ontology (dealing with questions about existence) is to demonstrate logical necessity that something must exist. The problem with this endeavor is that it can put the cart before a really big horse. Many of these ideas are abstract, and being thought necessary as a result of various arguments, these abstractions sometimes get unreasonably reified.

Generally speaking, I find the conflation of logic and reality to be an enormously common mistake, including in Platonism, which is something of a refined form of committing this error. Though this misunderstanding is not limited to those attempting to defend their beliefs in God, it is exceptionally common among them since, lacking credible evidence, philosophical arguments are often central to their efforts. These arguments essentially try to logic "God" into existence by showing that it is a logical necessity. Doing this for God's existence is, on the whole, playing word games.

Indeed, as weird as it is, a philosopher could prove "logical necessity" for the existence of some entity, say a deity, and yet no such entity must actually exist in reality. This claim sounds preposterous, but if the logical framework the philosopher is using doesn't really match reality, we can prove all sorts of things are logically necessary and yet physically meaningless. Abstract mathematics provides a useful window into this line of thought.

It is actually easy to think of examples of this kind of thing if one spends any serious time studying mathematics, particularly the math related to infinity. Take, for instance, numbers that are so large as to be essentially meaningless, and I'm not talking about cute little "big" numbers like googolplex (one with ten raised to the one-hundred power zeroes following it) or Skewes's or Graham's numbers (too big to succinctly describe, do look them up). Sure, those are fantastically big, but they're smaller than most.

There's an entire branch of mathematical philosophy, in fact, known as "ultrafinitism" that says that after some point, numbers really don't mean anything. Certainly, just because we can produce some sort of notation that indicates what they are, and because the axioms underlying number theory guarantee that they "exist" as abstractions, it is not incumbent upon the universe to produce or house any sort of structure that can be enumerated by every number. Indeed, it is easy to come up with numbers that dwarf any number that can represent the size of anything that a finite universe can create, at least without getting a bit too *ad hoc*. If ours is, indeed, finite, then as mathematical abstractions, there are numbers that are simply far too big to count anything both physical and interesting.[5] We could, for example, simply take the best data available, say estimating the total number of quantum states in a volume a few billion times that of the observable universe, and then for extreme overkill, raise it to Skewes's number power, or do so Skewes's number of times. In doing so, we leave meaning far, far behind and yet do not even yet show up on a map that extends "to infinity."

Other examples of unreal abstract ideas are copious: what do fractions of "super-large" numbers really mean in reality, like one over the huge number just described? How about "transcendental" irrational real numbers like π, especially the ones that *aren't* fundamental constants? Because π is important, we should perhaps treat it differently, but there are *uncountably many* transcendental irrational real numbers, the vast majority of which have no known physical meaning. Of course, one could argue that π must exist in the universe because of how useful it is, but that's not correct if very, very good approximations of it, say to

---

5   By considering varying combinations of things, and combinations of those combinations, and so on, as things themselves, we could get physical structures counted by numbers of any size we want, but these sorts of things lose any real sense of relevance far more quickly than "there's another number" does.

tens or millions or billions of decimal places, are actually what's really going on.

Back to abstractions we have no reason to believe are real, what about the infinitely many infinities? At some point, even if the universe is indeed infinite, logic dictates that there exist concepts with sizes that are literally beyond comprehension and salient meaning. Must these exist because logic says so? Or is it more reasonable to see logic as what it is: a construction that allows us to create an abstract representation of reality, rather like a map, and even extend it beyond reality's true boundaries?

To emphasize: "This must necessarily exist" only ensures that some abstraction "exists" in some abstract sense, and it "exists" then in a particular axiomatic framework. Particularly, "this must necessarily exist" confers no responsibility on reality whatsoever! Platonism should have a hard time weathering this storm.

Of importance is not just that reality is not dictated, or even influenced, by our logical constructions; it is that it is the other way around! We often see this clearly with really good illusions (like the illusion of intelligent design in the natural world). Our entire conception of logic has been built around the idea of how we attempt to make sense of the universe. Sure, we've extended that now into the purely abstract and rigidly formal, but all of our basic axioms (from which logical systems get their utility) ultimately have their grounding in our best guesses about reality itself.

Furthermore, the responsibility rests on our shoulders to realize that our abstract representations, though very, very useful, are still abstract representations of reality, not statements about reality itself. Our mathematics, our scientific theories, our models, our

Begging the question?

philosophical conjectures, and our theological ram-
blings are all abstract structures that we designed as
maps, or tools for map-making, to attempt to better
understand the terrain of the universe we find ourselves in. All along, it has been our system of
attempting to understand the world getting nudged
into a neater and neater fit, so far as we can tell, by
the brute force of a non-agent universe. (I'd say "an
indifferent universe," but some Christian apologists
have already proved to me that they try to exploit that
term as if I'm implying agency by saying "indifferent"—
sickeningly trite.)

Speaking of physical theories, we have ready ac-
cess to another interesting example. Now is an exciting
time of sorts because we face a problem in that our
highly successful map to understanding reality,
meaning logic, and its fruits, has run into one of these
places where, ultimately, we may have to reexamine
the foundations of our intellectual cartography.
Quantum mechanics very successfully explains
evidence from reality with the tools we have, but it
appears not to be able to be properly understood. It's
possible that nature doesn't really present the basis for
the kind of logic we've been pretending it does all
along. Indeed, brutish ideas like "the thing is here or it
is not" have hinged upon understanding our macroscopic experience of reality, which appears not to hold
at the sufficiently microscopic level. Quantum mechanics, then, makes for a good chance to impress the
lesson again: the universe (reality) is not subject to our
logic. Our logic is an abstract construct via which we
attempt to understand what actually is.

Physicists sometimes fall into this trap far enough
to believe the physical theories literally are reality.
Mathematicians do likewise, although mathematics is

both a map of its own and a collection of very useful map-making tools. Mathematical Platonists, and their more general brethren, confuse the map and the tools for the terrain of the universe. Put this way, it seems inane, but mathematical Platonism is very seductive.

The seduction of mathematical Platonism is that it really feels like mathematical objects and truths have some kind of independent existence. The reason is that they are axiomatic systems of idealized concepts with the property that once the axioms and logic are chosen, the entire abstract framework is defined. That is to say that the truth values of every proposition within the reach of the mathematical system are already determined, and mathematicians essentially explore the system to find those truth values. It has a real feeling of discovery to it, but the underlying axioms are where we made it up, to put it loosely. Since many of the simpler axioms are based on our "self-evident" experience of reality, the map closely matches the terrain, and it is easy to fall into the trap of thinking the description *is* reality.

It's very much like the children's board game called *Candyland*, which I'm about to ruin for all readers who must endure "playing" this game with interested children. In that game, there is a deck of cards that is shuffled, and then players take turns turning them over one at a time, following their instructions to move pieces around the board. Surprisingly, absolutely no decision making is involved in playing a game of *Candyland*. Thus, once the cards are shuffled, the game is over. "Playing" merely reveals what is already determined, however much it feels like playing a game. The game was actually played, in a sense, when the cards were shuffled, it just doesn't look or feel like it.

34

To elaborate briefly, what we refer to as "playing" a game of *Candyland* is really just methodically discovering the results of shuffling the cards before the game started. Similarly, mathematics is a process of determining truth values for statements that follow from basic formalized axioms. Once we choose the axioms and know what we are calling logic, the truth values of every statement within that system are already determined, though we don't know those values until we prove them.

I Agree

In other words, mathematics, which is in all ways more interesting than *Candyland*, can be seen as the effort of coming to understand certain classes of axiomatic systems, those being systems of propositions in which each proposition is assigned a truth value by some scheme known as a logic. Of key importance in this way of looking at mathematics is that the axiomatic systems are built upon the underlying axioms, statements that are abstracted from our experience of reality and from other abstractions and are then taken to be "self-evident."

Generally, we accept the fact that axioms are baldly asserted, and since this is true of all axiomatic systems, it is not a strike against any of them to point it out. Incidentally, religious apologists often like to assert that naturalism, the position that there is no supernatural, attempts to baldly assert that reality exists. So what? "Nature exists" is certainly more self-evident than is "God exists." Axioms have to be judged against how "self-evident" they really are, how useful they are, how little they assume, and in other such ways. This, then, is why the theistic worldview axioms seemed more reasonable in the past than now; we now see that the purported existence of God is not self-

35

evident, has limited utility with little or no explanatory power, and yet assumes an awful lot.

Indeed, in an axiomatic system, truth values are assigned with respect to the underlying axioms, and thus, in an important sense, these "absolute" truths aren't universal phenomena but rather are only as valid as the underlying axioms. Here, then, lies a big, but tangential, point: "truth," in the absolute mathematical sense, doesn't really mean anything except in terms of the underlying axioms, which are themselves abstractions. Once we know which logic we are using, then, and have determined a fundamental set of axioms, the locally-true "truth" of every proposition that can be examined from within that axiomatic system is already determined—although we know very, very few propositions worth examining and even fewer of the truth values. So, like playing *Candyland*, we have shuffled the cards and now get to start turning them over, though in mathematics we're not confined to the one-card-at-a-time process in the board game, and the game does not end by reaching a certain spot on the board. Importantly, the whole axiomatic system and all its truth values already "exist" once we've chosen the axioms and logic, so finding out truth values within it has a real sense of discovery to it.

So, mathematical Platonism, in a way, has some apparently reasonable appeal. Once we've chosen the axioms and the logic, the whole thing is built, and it's up to us to explore the system and discover the timeless truths contained within it, if we want to know them. Thus it feels like those truths exist and that we are discovering them, but this is because it is easy to lose sight of the fact that we made the whole system by choosing the axioms and logic. Also often lost in the shuffle, the axioms and logic are abstract things that do not "exist" in reality. They are abstract statements (hence their timelessness, incidentally—and yes, do draw the relevant analogy to an "eternal" God here) made in and shared by the minds of thinking beings who created them. We can explore them in a mental sense, and philosophers can continue to work on what that means, but it is certainly not the same meaning as Platonists would have us accept: that these ideas, the mathematics, exist as a part of reality itself for us to find therein.

Dot, Dot, Dot

3

Down the Rabbit Hole

In early February of 2013, I was having an email conversation with historian Richard Carrier. The discussion was about infinity, and it arose from his invitation for me to examine one of his arguments (discussed near the end of this collection) that uses the idea. It caused me to dig more deeply into the idea of infinity than I ever had needed to before, and that exploration led to the seeds of this book. Particularly, I was struck yet again by the sheer weirdness of the infinite. In fact, the way we've chosen to define our numbers runs us into of some of this paradoxical weirdness as soon as we think about it.

· · ·

Thinking upon the idea of infinity may lead someone to the opinion that the deeper into this rabbit hole one goes, the weirder the place gets. Perhaps Lewis Carroll wrote *Alice's Adventures in Wonderland,* a satire of abstract mathematics, a few decades too early, then, because abstract mathematics had not gotten properly weird until Georg Cantor made it so by blowing open the topic of infinity. This happened about a decade after *Alice's* publication and thereby sparked one of the most intense debates in the history of the philosophy of mathematics. This really is a deep, dark rabbit hole, and it is littered throughout with highly perplexing and uncomfortable paradoxes.

Of central importance to keep in the back of our minds is what we just discussed: that reality is not subject to logic but rather that logic has been built around our conception of reality. This creates a powerful illusion that our logic must be the way that it is because it is very, very difficult to conceive of a different way to do logic. That turns out not to be the case, though, which forms a deep, dark rabbit hole of its own.

At the moment, I'd like to elaborate upon the discussion that ended the first chapter, getting into more of the detail regarding the Peano Axioms and what followed. The Peano Axioms were devised specifically to put a formal foundation under arithmetic. Some of the Peano Axioms directly combine to give the idea that each number has a successor, literally exactly in the way that 1 follows 0, 2 follows 1, and $n+1$ follows n for any natural number n. This fact implies that there cannot be finitely many natural numbers because if there were, there would be a largest one, but every choice of would-be largest has a successor that is larger, a logical contradiction. Thus, the Peano Axioms predict the concept of infinity, but they do not give us a way to get there. Adding one always gives us another number, not infinity.

To make a point, it's sort of worse than that, though. Successorship is a very slow way to get anywhere with numbers. Exponentiation (raising numbers to "powers") is much, much, much faster. If we choose some natural number greater than one, say two, raising that number to successive powers gets big fast. At each stage using two as a base, we literally double the previous number! Just ten iterations of this process, and we're over one thousand; only twenty and we're over a million. But then, this raises the question of what "getting big" means.

To wit, if we look at this process, there is no end to the successive doublings that we can do. Suppose at some arbitrary point, we say that we're at a "big" number. Then the next step doubles it, and our "big" number is only half as big as where we are now. Repeat ten times, and our "big" number is small like one is to one thousand. Repeat ten more times, and our "big" number is like one to a million. Feeling small yet? If we choose to select this new "bigger" number as "big," we would just do it all again because the choice of "big" was arbitrary in the first place. To say that some number is the largest power of two that we can use is identical to saying that there is a largest number, which the Peano Axioms preclude. Thus, successive multiplication by any number (here: using two as a model) still only gets us to another number at every step, never to infinity.

This concept, that we can "never get to infinity" from the Peano Axioms, has been refined quite a bit—and is its own source of philosophical controversy—and we now say that the infinity that "counts" the natural numbers, "countable infinity," represents a *strong limit cardinal*, meaning that it is a cardinal number (a number that enumerates sets) that cannot be reached either by succession or exponentiation.

Here's the paradox, then: when we go to build set theory from number theory, the Peano Axioms predict an infinite set of natural numbers, {1,2,3,...}, but the set theory that comes out of the Peano Axioms requires the negation of the axiom of infinity, essentially because "getting to" infinity is impossible from below. We cannot complete any infinite set via the Peano Axioms. This issue is part of the Pandora's-like Box

41

that Cantor opened, leading to David Hilbert dedicating some of his famous questions (twenty-three unsolved questions listed in 1900 as the most important ones for twentieth-century mathematics) to its resolution. It took Kurt Gödel's Incompleteness Theorems forty years later to tell us that from within the Peano Axioms we cannot decide if infinity exists or not. The result led to a reformulation of set theory according to the Zermelo-Fraenkel Axioms of set theory, which, again, essentially make for the accepted foundation today.

The Zermelo-Fraenkel Axioms include the axiom of infinity, which immediately implies that there exists at least one infinite set. Incidentally, per Gödel, this raises other questions that themselves cannot be answered from within the Zermelo-Fraenkel axiomatic system. As we might expect, following this progression so far, adding more axioms leads to more unresolvable questions that lead to choices about more axioms, and this may continue *ad infinitum.*

This tells us two very important things: (1) claiming that "infinity exists" is equivalent to accepting the axiom of infinity, and (2) all of this takes on a very peculiar human-made feel when examined closely, precisely because it is human-made. Indeed, it would still be human-made if observations vindicated some physical reality of infinity, which they have not yet done and may not be able to do, perhaps even if it's true.

The first point just above means that infinity is an abstraction defined by an axiom. The way we "get to" infinity (remember, it is a strong limit cardinal) is by defining it. This leads to a whole fringe group within the philosophy of mathematics called "ultrafinitism" that rejects the axiom of infinity—possibly for what are

42

ultimately good reasons. Fringe or not, following mathematician Jan Mycielski, ultrafinitists have shown that mathematics can be done, if necessary, without assuming the existence of infinity. (It's worth noting that finitist and ultrafinitist mathematical methods may incur a larger up-front cost to understand and employ, so an argument that infinity is a worthwhile simplifying assumption, or fiction, is warranted in rebuttal, with Mycielski's work showing that it may not matter in practical terms which map we use for this terrain.[6])

On the other extreme, it leads to other fringe groups of mathematicians—also possibly for good reasons—who argue for expansions of our number systems to very bizarre concepts like John Conway's "surreal numbers." (Go take a moment to look that up, read, feel dizzy, and agree that "surreal" is a really good name for them.) Other branches of non-standard analysis also exist, along with some strange ideas that suggest that there could be more strong limit cardinals beyond the infinitely many infinities themselves, possibly an infinite progression of such hyper-inaccessible sizes of "things." Frankly, and to put it as plainly as it deserves, this shit gets weird.

This all hopefully highlights the second point, the humanness of this whole enterprise. For now, for all we know, infinity is an *abstract concept* made and existing only in the minds of those who can imagine it. Indeed, this is the mainstream interpretation of infinity among mathematicians: it's an abstraction—a useful

---

6   For more information, see Lavine, Shaughan (1994), *Understanding the Infinite*, Boston: Harvard University Press. Mycielski's theorem is discussed on p. 273.

43

one—that represents the idea embodied by the Peano Axioms of "can't say only finitely many," and it "exists" only as such, as an axiomatically defined abstraction. This is the camp I find myself in, intrigued by the fringe groups who explore infinity otherwise but not swayed to any of their causes.

And so we return to the argument that it is *we* who judge the worth of our axioms, usually by comparing them to the real world in some way. Here, then, we face the question of physical infinities: can/do infinite things exist in reality? This question is not settled and is rather hotly debated. It also raises the question of what the larger infinities would mean in reality: do they also exist?

As it turns out, the easiest approach to claiming that physical infinities exist is fraught with the same problem presented by the strong limit cardinal property that creates the question about them in the first place. It has been suggested, for instance, that unless something were to destroy it, the universe may necessarily have an infinite timeline, at least in one direction, because at the moment T presumed to be the last moment, there is the moment $T+1$ later than it (in whatever units). On the other hand, though, at any given time T, no matter how long it has been, the universe is still only finitely older than it was when we began measuring—it never becomes infinitely older. There's that strong limit cardinal thing again; there is simply no way to get to infinity without jumping to it, which is the same as accepting a particular axiom, which is not proving "existence" in actuality. Philosophers and even physicists will refer to a "global" frame in which the entirety of the timeline and spatial scope of the universe can be assessed at once, but importantly, we cannot know what that looks like. This precludes us from making the argument that the universe has an infinite timeline or physical size, and it also precludes apologists like William Lane Craig from convincingly arguing that the universe cannot be infinitely old.

Additionally, there is the question of actual infinities, meaning abstract infinities that do not need to exist physically and yet possess quantitative meaning. Abstract infinities, like those accepted by the vast majority of mathematicians, are considered "actual" infinities, despite the poor terminology. Rejecting actual infinities, even just abstractly existing objects with infinite sizes, creates hard questions that butt against the Peano Axioms like "What is the largest meaningful number?" It may not matter, though; the map just isn't the terrain.

For my purposes, this is very powerful. If those who believe in God want to claim it has infinite properties, which they must to maintain statuses like "Most High" and "Almighty," which they do by official dogma, then we have to wonder what they are implying about their deity. It seems to follow that God, thusly defined, condemned to abstract unreality, at the very least unless physical infinities can be proven to exist. Critically, though, as I keep saying, abstractions don't do anything except serve as the basis for potentially useful ideas. Particularly, abstractions don't have agency and thus can't create, destroy, judge, forgive, or answer prayers.

If believers want to claim instead that their God is finite, then that's a major concession for them to make. It puts them in a rather serious bind, not least that they're stuck back into the memetic arms race that may have made them play the infinity card in the first place. Anyone else could come along and assert a bigger God, and the only recourse is to inflate their own. They become very vulnerable in this position for the same reason the Peano Axioms are unresolvable with set theory: here, infinite Gods cannot exist but neither can there be a limit on finite ones if they are truly to be omni-grade Gods.

Interestingly, believers remain in this arms race for bigness anyway, once they understand the implications of the Zermelo-Fraenkel Axioms include an infinite progression of infinities. Only now they have to argue it on ever more abstruse concepts. This—that God is an abstraction, not an entity with agency, particularly if it is said to have any infinite properties— is a big point I wanted to make in my book *God Doesn't; We Do*. This fundamental problem has the result of making their arguments less and less coherent and more and more obviously in the realm of "making stuff up," and isn't good for their cause.

4

Craigian Infinity

William Lane Craig. His name could be its own sentence—not for his notable contributions to the discussion about "God," but for his notorious abuses in debating his case. To focus only upon infinity, Craig has made a substantial part of his career attempting to defend the now-famous Kalām Cosmological Argument for the existence of a (Deistic) creator God. To do so he needs to attempt to establish that the Universe did, indeed, have a beginning, and so he expends a lot of effort trying to debunk the idea of actual infinities. It would be so much easier for him if he could admit that God is simply an abstraction, but he cannot do so without conceding theism. This chapter seeks to clarify some of these matters.

$\bullet \ \bullet \ \bullet$

Prolific Christian apologist William Lane Craig and his Craigian followers are very fond of employing the Kalām Cosmological Argument for the existence of "God."[7] In order to apply it, since one of its premises is that the Universe began to exist, they are forced to attempt to eliminate any philosophical possibility for physical and actual infinities. Incidentally, they may

---

[7]   Indeed, Craig has given a book-length defense of it: Craig, William Lane (2000), *The Kalām Cosmological Argument*, Eugene, Oregon: Wipf and Stock.

find this collection very useful to that end, although it would be highly disingenuous of them to use it for that purpose—I reject the Kalām argument entirely.

The Kalām argument, which was borrowed from Muslim apologists who themselves got it from Aristotle, has been soundly refuted and therefore need not be repeated here. Interested readers can find it along with my comparison of it to Russell's Paradox in the sixth chapter of my own *God Doesn't; We Do*, for example. Other critiques of the argument can be found in numerous places, pointing out its equal applicability to every theistic religion that claims a creator, for example. My focus here is on part of the uses and abuses of the idea of infinity, which Craigians use to claim the premise that the Universe began is necessarily true—again a possible confusion of map and terrain based upon philosophical necessity.

There are a few issues that might leap out here and distract us from my core endeavor. First, for readers casually familiar with modern physics, there is the apparently glaring issue that the idea that "the universe began" at some point in the past may not be an issue of contention, with two important caveats. In fact, physicists have given us an approximate date for the occurrence, at least for the part of the Cosmos we can observe, some 13.8 billion years ago. This raises the question of why Craig needs to go through the entire rigmarole of talking about actual infinities in the first place.

The first caveat to this point answers the question of Craig's behavior. It is that we actually do not know what happened before the universe cooled enough to become transparent. Indeed, our physical models break down at that point, and it has even been suggested that we *cannot* know for sure what happened before then, including the possibility that the universe existed indefinitely, or infinitely, long before that time in some unknown state. The "Big Bang" is predicated on a theory that does not take quantum effects into account, and so it may not be the strict beginning point that Craig needs. There are even growing movements within the physics community that contest the idea that the universe began at all, for instance the loop quantum gravity and string theory proponents. Which models of physics will win out in these debates is still up in the air, and that fact is important enough to negate Craig's ability to lean upon whatever event occurred some 13.8 billion years ago as a true beginning of the universe.

The second caveat, of course, is that "the universe" doesn't have only one meaning, a point I will try to clarify slightly by capitalizing the more-encompassing idea of Universe: everything that is, was, or ever will be, as we'd see it if examined from a global frame (outside of the Universe). I find it essentially impossible to conceive of this idea with any clarity.

At any rate, I do not think it is my station here to do more than introduce the general idea of this line of argumentation with physicists. The reason Craigians need their gymnastics, however, is tied to it; they cannot accept the modern physics interpretation of time and make their case. The preponderance of modern physicists now subscribe to what is known as the B-Theory of time, which says that space and time are bound together as different dimensional aspects of one phenomenon we call spacetime.

On the B-Theory of time, there is no meaning to the idea of "before" the beginning of the universe, supposing our present models are correct, as that would be, if such a thing happened, the event from which space and time came. There is no "before" any hypothetical beginning of the universe because there was no temporal dimension that could qualify (or quantify) "before" that event. As an implication, even an eternal creator God couldn't have created the universe *before this time* because "before this time" doesn't mean anything, not to mention that creating requires something to work on or with, which also presumably did not exist at that time.

This idea, of course, feels weird. In fact, it leads many of us to suspect that it is conceivable that our spacetime is embedded in a larger Universe, which could be expected to have a (possibly independent) temporal dimension to it, but admitting this has two problems for Craigians. First, it suggests natural causes of our universe are possible, and second, it simply drives the problem another step back, raising the question of how, and if, the capital-U Universe began.

Craigians, because they want to defend an eternal God, reject the modern B-Theory of time in favor of the A-Theory of time,[8] which is essentially how time was thought of before spacetime was a concept in its own right. In the A-Theory of time, there is some kind of overarching Universal meta-time upon which our temporal dimension may be dependent, or not, and in this formulation, "before the beginning of time" is still a meaningful period in which causes could engender effects. The Kalām argument depends upon the A-

---

8   See, for instance, Craig, William Lane, "God, Time, and Creation," *Reasonable Faith with William Lane Craig*, http://www.reasonablefaith.org/god-time-and-creation (accessed 18 Sept., 2013).

Theory of time because otherwise the question doesn't even make sense and nothing could have acted to create the Universe. (Do note, the Kalām doesn't seek to prove Christianity or its God, just that there was some "uncaused first cause." It also doesn't explain how creation was performed on nothing, save to simply assert it as one of God's defining powers.)

The problem is that on the A-Theory of time, we cannot simply say that the Universe has a beginning because there is no good reason for it. An eternal Universe is hardly different—and more parsimonious—than an eternal agent God. They protest that the Universe cannot be consistently asserted to exist as a brute fact and then yet attempt to do that very thing for their more-complex God, losing the detail in the weeds of thorny philosophical arguments to a deity's "necessity."

There they are stuck, then, since there is as much evidence that the Universe itself is eternal on the A-Theory of time as there is that it had a beginning some finite time in the past as there is that an eternal God exists. Indeed, a lack of actual physical infinities (of stuff) need not preclude the existence of an actual temporal infinity. That is, the Universe could actually potentially exist eternally even if it cannot include an infinite quantity of anything. These facts neuter the Kalām completely.

Ignoring that, the typical Craigian approach is to attempt to declare "absurd" the notion of actual infinities, thereby requiring a moment of creation.[9] To

---

9   Craig, William Lane, "Forming an Actual Infinite by Successive Addition," *Reasonable Faith with William Lane Craig*,

be fair, Craig surmises correctly that if there are no actual infinities, and if the A-Theory of time is correct, then there is some point only finitely long in the past at which the Universe began. Fairness stops, though, when he inserts a creator as a "necessary" element of that beginning, and, of course, as an evangelical apologist, tries to tie that creator to Yahweh and the character of Jesus.

The Kalām argument, in fact, only tries to bridge the gap between "began" and "was caused," which is far less than Craig needs, and, as has been pointed out in many ways, it apparently fails to do so. For an example of my own making, so far as I can tell, the Kalām Argument seems to commit category error in which the Universe is taken to be a thing within itself, this being how I identified it with Russell's Paradox in *God Doesn't; We Do.* The Kalām asserts that "everything that began has a cause," but can the Universe be considered something within that "everything"? It is utterly unclear that it can be.

The Craigian use of infinity also commits some of the errors typical of people who conflate the idea of infinity with actually being a number, despite his surprising care with the topic in other regards. In essence, they note correctly that counting backwards from the present moment cannot get us to (negative) infinity.[10] I would argue that, though correct, this

---

http://www.reasonablefaith.org/forming-an-actual-infinite-by-successive-addition (accessed 18 Sept. 2013).

[10] Craig, William Lane, "Counting Down from Infinity," *Reasonable Faith with William Lane Craig*, http://www.reasonablefaith.org/counting-down-from-infinity (accessed 18 Sept. 2013).

points to one of the largest flaws in this line of thinking. It essentially assumes what it wants to prove: a beginning of the Universe. Their conclusion that the Universe must have had a beginning because it would be impossible for an infinite number of moments to have passed already, though, commits the error of jumping over the ellipsis straight to the strong limit cardinal of (negative) infinity. It does so by inserting the idea that the Universe had to have a beginning either "at" time negative infinity or at some point only finitely long ago. Note the circularity here: this line of thinking implicitly assumes what it wants to establish.

Having a temporally infinite universe, on the A-Theory of time, simply means that however far back we look, even in principle, there is further back that could be looked—here, infinity is better understood qualitatively. Humorously, this is exactly the kind of infinity, a "potential infinity," that Craig attempts to defend as part of the essential nature of God and the possible *future* state of the Universe.[11] As so often happens when seeking to make an argument, it appears Craig wants it both ways—potential infinities one way but not the way that would interfere with his case.

Of course, the temptation to step outside of this local-frame mindset and leap to a notion of a "beginning" as an anchor is overwhelming, but if the Universe really is infinite in scope in the negative temporal dimension, that leap isn't just impossible, it's meaningless. In other words, the Craigian argument,

---

[11]   Craig attempts to deal with this issue on his website: Craig, William Lane, "God and Infinity," *Reasonable Faith with William Lane Craig*, http://www.reasonablefaith.org/god-and-infinity (accessed 18 Sept. 2013).

even on the A-Theory of time, has no purchase without jumping outside of a framework that has no outside.

There is, though, another important point. The Craigian argument against actual infinities presents another glaring problem: the omni-grade properties of the Christian God for which they apologize depend upon infinity. Omni-grade properties are often taken to mean "infinite in scope," particularly omnipotence and omniscience. The Craigian solution to this problem is to argue for a qualitative, not quantitative, understanding of infinity, which would make him something of an finitist—people who reject the notion of infinity as a quantity, even in the abstract.

Very few mathematicians are finitists, though, and there are good reasons. One reason is that infinity, even as a qualitative thing, has roots in the quantitative. Since Cantor, very, very few mathematicians treat infinity purely qualitatively: the infinities quantify various sizes of infinite sets, even if they do not have concrete existence. Infinity, qualitatively, is the idea of being without bound, usually without maximum, and this monolithic notion is not sufficient to cover the gamut of ideas that consequentially follow the acceptance of the axiom of infinity. Theologians using infinity, again, seem to want it both ways. They want to say there is infinity—in God—but not deal with the consequences of accepting the axiom that allows it.

Let's look at these various ideas applied to omni-grade properties given to God. Here, it is taken to mean "the most conceivably possible." The glaring problem with this formulation is that "the most conceivably possible" is not just that it is obviously vague, it is that the moment any value is specified, that amount is no longer "the most conceivably possible." In some cases, Craigian apologists can

54

equivocate here more easily than others. For example, a fairly easy case can be made for a qualitatively infinite understanding of God's omni-benevolence. This looks like a big con of the argument-to-ignorance type, though, since benevolence is clearly hard to measure quantitatively. For instance, power and knowledge are not nearly so hard to quantify, leaving Craigian defenses of these qualitative descriptions of the core ideas of omnipotence and omniscience severely lacking. Particularly, the questions of whether or not "God" could do one more thing, move one ounce more, or know one more detail are left hanging and said to be meaningless questions.

A particular case that gets brought up often is whether or not omniscient "God" knows all of the infinitely many decimal places of irrational constants like π (this being *only* a countable infinity!).[12] The rather weak defense of this is to claim that there are abstract infinities that apply to things like numbers, and knowledge of these isn't really God's business since "God is actual." This question-begging statement rather severely limits the concept of omniscience, however, and raises uncomfortable questions of whether or not "God" knows the newly found decimal values of π before the first computer calculates them. There is no point at which apologists like Craig can argue that God doesn't know the next value since a computer can conceivably calculate it eventually. Additionally, if such a computer, which need not be

---

[12]   Craig attempts to deal with this: Craig, William Lane, "Does God Know an Actually Infinite Number of Things?" *Reasonable Faith with William Lane Craig*, http://www.reasonablefaith.org/does-god-know-an-actually-infinite-number-of-things (accessed 18 Sept. 2013).

very complex, were *eternal* and outside of time, like apologists argue of God, then the computer would have calculated *every* value. Shouldn't God be able to calculate every value, then? What, I wonder, is being said about God with their evasive argument?

Eternalness is another omni-grade property of God that raises bigger issues for theologians than they are often pressed with. Indeed, the only concepts that we call timeless, other than "God," are abstractions, built from axioms, such as mathematical "truths." It seems quite a bit like special pleading to claim that "God" is the only actually timeless thing in existence, all other eternal objects being so for the reason that they are abstractions. It shouldn't be surprising to note that Platonism confuses this matter profoundly.

Qualitative infinities cannot get apologists out of these problems. It is easy to say that "infinity is the quality of being without limit," but it is very difficult to say what that means. Mathematicians argued about this point for centuries without much mooring until the axiom of infinity was introduced. Because there is no evidence for actual infinities, it was hardly welcomed with fanfare, but the axiom started to allow mathematicians to answer a lot of long-standing questions. The result was a revolution in the branch of mathematics called analysis that was every bit as substantial as was the theory of relativity in physics (occurring at around the same time) and it allowed hard problems with real-world applicability to be answered at a theoretical level.

This progress came at a price, though: infinity could no longer merely be considered a quality, and yet it isn't precisely a quantity in the numerical sense either. Each infinity enumerates innumerable sets that by conventional understanding *should* be bigger or

56

smaller than each other *but that are not.* On the other hand, each infinity *is* bigger or smaller than all the others and bigger than every finite value. The qualitative-quantitative line becomes gray and fuzzy, and the dichotomy breaks. I would argue that since infinity is an abstraction, it doesn't matter much.

Infinity makes sense as an abstraction and need not make physical sense to do so. Indeed, I feel the same way about "God." I have few qualms, except with the impact of the metaphor, with thinking of "God" as an abstract construction (possessing no agency). Who would worship, evangelize, murder, or die for that? The difference between Craigians and me is that they want to argue that their favorite abstraction, "God," is actual while infinities are not. I'm content to leave these ideas in the fascinating but immaterial abstract. Indeed, I feel like this is the only way to make "God" anything remotely close to "real."

Dot, Dot, Dot

• • •
Infinity is Weird
• • •

An underlying goal I have with this project is to expose some of the inordinate weirdness that is deeply tied into thinking about the infinite. As a mathematician, I had been familiarized with some of this uncanny lack of intuitiveness, the relatively famous Hilbert's Hotel example (see Glossary) and the likes, but as I dug more deeply into the topic, I found some of it absolutely staggeringly strange. I am particularly impressed that because of its inherent peculiarity, we are required to use great caution in employing arguments that invoke the infinite with regards to the real world if we want to have a real chance of employing it accurately. This section endeavors to make clear, but hardly scratches the surface of, the impenetrable depths with which infinity just doesn't line up with our experience in reality. This pushes my thinking further toward the idea that infinity is an abstract concept. As a result, the combination of infinity and God is incoherent, as is any argument that relies upon it; or it forces God to be an abstraction as well.

Dot, Dot, Dot

5

All Numbers and All Infinities Are Very Small

Of everything included here, this is perhaps the best section to really get a sense of how unintuitive (read: weird) the idea of infinity is. I also consider this idea to be of rather profound importance within this topic, so much so that I seriously contemplated naming the book for the theme presented here. The idea I am sharing here is deceptively simple, obvious, and yet in many ways revolting to our "better" sense. I hope that you enjoy contemplating it as much as I have.

• • •

One rather bizarre truth that we must face if we accept the infinitude of numbers is that all numbers are very small—or put another way, every number is smaller than most. In fact, it's even more accurate, if less eloquent, to say that every number is smaller than almost every one of them. There are a number of ways to think about this concept that turn out to be very useful for getting one's head around this very non-intuitive notion. I wish to present some of them, but first I'd like to take a moment to discuss intuitiveness in this regard.

We use the phrase "large numbers" quite frequently, and in fact, I'll argue that while it has no meaning mathematically to say so, it frequently does have salience to talk about large numbers. Some aboriginal cultures have apparently captured this notion. The Walpiri, a tribe from Australia, is famous for having no counting words beyond two, using a "one, two, many" system instead where every number greater than two is simply described as "many." Incidentally, studies have shown that these people can count, when it comes to it, but they lack number words beyond a certain point.

This is not so strange except in setting the limit at two. In English, we only have names for numbers that are conceivably useful, with some extensions using prefixes attached to -illion after a time. By the time we reach numbers with a few scores of digits, we also run out of names for them except in special cases, even if we can represent them numerically. We have a name for huge numbers like the googolplex (the number written with a one followed by the number of zeroes that is a one with one hundred zeroes after it), but what do we call, for instance, the number with one less zero than that? That idea—that we've only named numbers that are, to speak very vaguely, conceivably useful—provides the clue to finding salience in our concept of "large numbers." We can call numbers "large" when they're relatively large given the context.

These numbers we're naming, or even the ones beyond names, though, are not large in an absolute sense as mathematical abstractions devoid of context. While one quadrillion (one thousand trillion, that is, one with fifteen zeroes following it) dollars constitutes a very large number of dollars, one quadrillion is nothing compared against the vast majority (almost all, as it turns out) of the natural numbers. If we take any "large" number, say one quadrillion, and multiply it by one hundred, the result obviously dwarfs our original "large" number by one hundred to one, casting a shadow over what it meant to be "large" in the first place. But there's no mathematical reason that we have to limit ourselves to multiplying by one hundred. We could multiply by a quadrillion, or multiply by a quadrillion a quadrillion times, by which time our original "large" number is lost in a sea of far, far larger values. When we realize that one quadrillion was chosen arbitrarily, meaning that any number, including a quadrillion multiplied by itself a quadrillion times, could replace our initial choice with the same implications, we get an idea of what is meant by every number being very small.

These abstractions are hard to understand and very high-minded, bordering on the feel of nonsense. Sometimes it is useful to try to get our heads around these numbers, but this is very difficult to do. For instance, one quadrillion is roughly the number of grains of refined, white sugar that could be hauled in 134 full-sized (53-foot) tractor-trailers. That's (kind of) a lot of sugar, but bear in mind that this number is only 1,000,000,000,000,000 in our condensed notation.

To get an idea of the size of a quadrillion multiplied by itself a quadrillion times, we'd have to have a one followed by fifteen quadrillion zeroes just to write the number in the same very condensed notation (incidentally, this number is still inconceivably smaller than the googolplex). In 12-point font on standard 8.5-inch by 11-inch paper (with one-inch margins), printed on both sides of the paper, just writing down a quadrillion multiplied by itself a quadrillion times requires a stack of papers filled entirely with zeroes roughly 250,000 kilometers thick, that is, reaching 65% of the way to the moon! Again, that's just writing the number down in a standard, somewhat condensed notation.

63

Bear in mind again that writing down a quadrillion merely takes roughly two inches on one line of the page and yet represents the number of grains of sugar that could be carried by a small fleet of full-sized semi-trucks. Now remember that even a ridiculously, impossible-to-understand large number like a quadrillion multiplied by itself a quadrillion times is a pittance that amounts to essentially nothing. Indeed, a number represented by a book of concatenated zeroes reaching from here to the sun or to the Andromeda Galaxy, which are hardly any distances at all, leave a quadrillion to the quadrillionth power minuscule beneath even potential notice (and are still themselves inconceivably smaller than the googolplex, which has more than a thousand quadrillion times more zeroes than the estimated number of atoms in the observable universe).

The fact of the matter is that these numbers, when bereft of real-world context, are impossible to call "large." Indeed, they are unimaginably small. Incredibly, this smallness is a property that applies to every single number there is. Even more incredibly, this implies, as we've discussed, that against the infinite, every number is equally small, which is to say infinitely small.

There is a humorously named mathematical result that may be one of the best tools for getting some mental purchase on how big infinity really is, driving home this point that every number is smaller than almost all numbers. That theorem is known as "the infinite monkey theorem," taking its name from a hypothetical scenario in which we might say "an army of monkeys bangs away on typewriters for some very long period of time." Real monkeys aren't involved in the theorem, of course, and apparently an examination has revealed that "monkeys" (chimpanzees, actually, which are apes, not monkeys) tend not to type randomly, apparently choosing preferences for certain keys over others. Indeed, I once read that at least one chimpanzee in the test produced several pages filled mostly with the letter S.

At any rate, the infinite monkey theorem evaluates the idea of properly random strings of concatenated characters from some character library. The result states that, on the assumption that the string of characters is infinitely long, the probability is one, almost surely—indicating all-but certainty—that every *possible* result will appear. Impossible results, of course, are not expected nor required to appear. For example if the character set did not contain the letter E for some reason, we would have no ability to conclude that the letter E would appear anywhere in the string. This theorem produces some rather incredible corollaries worth highlighting here. For the purpose, we will assume that all of the necessary typographical characters, including all relevant special characters, are included in the library.

First of all, we can conclude with certainty what the loose, commonly stated version of the infinite monkey theorem asserts: the entire text of William Shakespeare's *Hamlet* will certainly occur perfectly somewhere within an infinite string of sufficiently diverse typographical characters. What gives a sense of how large infinity is here is pausing to consider how far into the string of random typographical characters we'd have to go to find it. Getting even a single perfect short phrase, say "To be, or not to be, that is the question" would take astronomical amounts of paper— roughly one full page for each atom in the Milky Way Galaxy.

Indeed, infinity is big enough to accommodate far more than this. Not just *Hamlet* but also the entire collection of all of Shakespeare's works would eventually appear too, as would the entire collection of all of the books in the entire Library of Congress, not just in some order, but in *every conceivable order*, back to back if necessary. This insanely unlikely and long result would appear somewhere in the string after unimaginably many meaningless typographical debris and partial, but failed, attempts to produce this string, making the total number of characters required to get it to happen once fully beyond comprehension—and yet enumerable by our handy infinite-capacity abstract number system. Infinity is amply large to accommodate enough characters to guarantee this effectively impossible result.

And then, just to drive this point home, note that after it appears, there are still infinitely many characters left in the infinite string (with that astronomically large number up to that point being completely negligible)! Thus, we can conclude that it will happen not just the once but again sometime later. Then, after that, again. So, in an infinite string of randomly generated typographical characters there are enough characters so that the full text of every book in the entire Library of Congress, back to back in every conceivable order, would appear *infinitely many times*! Infinity isn't just big, then, and it's not even just incomprehensibly big. It's actually bigger than that.

As huge as infinity hopefully feels now, surprisingly, this fact also applies to the infinite itself! As discussed previously, once we accept the notion that there is a single infinite set, we have to face the fact that there are infinitely many sizes of infinity. However we decide to characterize those various sizes of infinity, the same result that applies to numbers applies here as well: every infinity is smaller than most. In a sense, in fact, it's actually a more powerful statement for the various infinite cardinalities than with numbers.

To elaborate briefly, with numbers we are able to obtain any number from any other number via successorship, that is to say from adding one over and over again. Indeed, this idea is the conceptual definition of the operation of addition. An implication of that is that given any nonzero number, the proportion of the smaller to the larger is never zero. Five is only a very tiny proportion of a quadrillion to the quadrillionth power, but that proportion is *not zero*. This situation does not apply with infinities.

The proportion in the situation of infinities has to be handled more carefully, and the idea can be managed via measure theory, an abstract analogue of measuring sizes. What we find is that when a smaller infinite set is embedded within a larger infinite set, as with the natural numbers inside the real numbers, the measure of the smaller infinite set *is* zero—a fact also true of any finite collection weighed against an infinite one containing it. Loosely, what this means is that each size of infinity amounts essentially to nothing compared with larger infinite cardinalities. Thus, in a meaningful sense, to climb the ladder of sizes of infinity is (infinitely) more substantial than going from any number to any bigger number. Still, however many steps up we take, there are infinitely more ahead of us, and on the acceptance of particular axioms, only finitely many behind us.

Here, then, we see that every number and every infinite cardinality is smaller than most. A direct implication is that any conception of "God" that relies upon claims of infinite amounts of quantifiable attributes like power or knowledge—others being conceivably quantifiable with careful metrics—is also necessarily smaller than most. Truly, the word "most" doesn't capture the fullness of meaning here. The accurate term is "almost all," which is far more than most.

The theological relevance of this statement hits hard upon the ontological definition of "God" as "Most High" given by Anselm in the eleventh century and explains much of William Lane Craig's philosophical chicanery on the topic of infinity. Anselm's "God" is that than which nothing higher can be conceived (see Chapter 16 for more on this important point). Therein lies his problem: we immediately realize that the moment we conceive of the highness of some conception of "God," not only can we conceive of something higher, as "highness" implies a metric at least in principle, but the "God" we have conceived of is lower than almost every conceivable conception. This is true if "God" is rendered as finite in "highness," and it is true if "God" is rendered as infinite in "highness." There is no escaping the simple reality that Anselm's conception of "God," upon which his ontological "proof" rests, is fatally flawed at the definition.

6

Infinite Divisibility and Strong Limit Cardinals

Maybe we cannot get out to infinity by any means other than by jumping there, but what about cutting things down to size? Particularly, what if we were to take an imaginary rod of some given length and cut it again and again until we have an *infinitesimal* length? Wouldn't we then have infinitely many pieces of the rod? Here I want to explore this question, including how we would have to go about cutting something into infinitesimal pieces.

. . .

Some philosophers like to argue that infinities are actualized by infinite divisibility. The usual statement follows along these lines. "Imagine we have a rod of some length and divide it in half, then divide the halves in half, then divide each piece in half over and over again. Can we continue to do this or not, and if not, why not?"

Well, without getting into physical concerns, this being a philosophical discussion about abstractions—an important distinction to keep in mind—sure, we can. The relevant follow-up question to ask, however, is "but at what point have we divided the rod into an infinite number of pieces?" The answer to that question is that we never have. ✓

The relevant question here is whether or not we see the jump that always occurs when people are ready to leap to actual infinities. It can be quite subtle, after all. Let's look at the process closely and see what has happened. After one cut, there are two pieces, and then after two cuts, there are four. Another cut yields eight, and the one after that gives thirty-two. After just twenty cuts, the rod is broken into 1,048,576 pieces, each less than one millionth the original length of the rod. After twenty more, each of those 1,048,576 pieces has been cut into 1,048,576 pieces of its own. (We might note that only after roughly 32 or 33 such bisecting cuts on a rod one meter long, we're to individual atoms.) In principle, ignoring physical limitations, this process can be continued indefinitely, but at any point along the way, we have only managed to bisect all pieces of the rod some number of times, say x, resulting in two to the power x pieces of rod, each the relevant fraction (two to the power of $-x$) of the original length of the rod. *Never* have we cut the rod into infinitely many pieces. *Never* do the pieces have infinitesimal length.

The jump goes like always in these cases: we can imagine cutting it once, or twice, or a hundred, or a million, or really any number of times, but the only way to get from this conception of a process to having it cut infinitely many times is to jump to it and assert that infinitely many cuts have already happened. Because infinity is a strong limit cardinal, there is no procedural way to get to infinity by repeated addition (successorship) or exponentiation, which is what repeated halving turns out to be. So can we, in principle, cut a rod of some finite length as many times as we wish? Sure. Can we keep doing that and get to infinitely many cuts? No. The only way to get to infinitely many cuts is to start with infinitely many cuts, which requires us to accept that "infinitely many"

70

is an enumerative quantity, which is to say to accept the axiom of infinity. To use the argument of repeated cuts to establish that we can use infinity as if it exists in actuality is therefore circular.

This situation may put the reader in mind of Zeno's famous Dichotomy Paradox that essentially claims that movement is illusory because in order to cross any distance, one must first cross half of it, which also applies to the half, and to half of that, etc., on down infinitely. The problem arises because, as Zeno argued, one cannot ever complete an infinite number of tasks (because countable infinity is a strong limit cardinal, though Zeno did not say so). The conclusion of this argument, the impossibility of movement, is apparently easily refuted—and famously was by Diogenes the Cynic—simply by getting up and walking across the room, but refuting the conclusion of an argument doesn't point out why it is incorrect.

Many people learn in a first-year calculus course that this paradox is resolved by the idea of convergent infinite series, that is that sums with infinitely many terms can sometimes add to a finite value. Indeed, the successive powers of one-half Zeno used, starting with the first power, add to one. The implication is that this sort of infinite process is, indeed, resolvable. Unfortunately, this solution does not necessarily address the problem at the center of the paradox: even if they are summable to a finite value, one cannot complete an infinite number of tasks.

One potential solution to Zeno's Dichotomy Paradox is simply that either of physical or actual infinities do not exist. This solution resolves the paradox by pointing out that an infinite number of tasks cannot be required because there cannot be infinitely many tasks, either conceptually (for actual infinities) or in reality (for physical infinities). Of course, as we've seen, this approach can be argued to create other issues. Fascinatingly, despite these and a plethora of other proposed solutions, Zeno's Dichotomy Paradox is not considered to have been solved.

To strike a bit more to the center of the problem, consider the Thomson's lamp construction put forth by British philosopher James F. Thomson in the 1950s. Thomson asks us to imagine a decidedly unrealistic lamp that can turn on and off more quickly than physical limitations would allow. In fact, he imagines that this lamp is set up to be on for thirty seconds, then off for fifteen seconds, then on again for seven and a half seconds, then off again for three and three quarters seconds. The lamp continues switching on and off thusly, at time intervals exactly half as long in each step as in the previous. Again, the series (in the time variable) here converges, so the lamp finishes its on/off cycling at exactly one minute from when it was turned on the first time. Thomson asks us whether the lamp is on or off at the end of this minute.

Both answers are wrong, however much we wail that one answer "has to" be right. The infinite-series argument is the main reason that Thomson's lamp is paradoxical, and so it cannot be seen as the valid solution to the analogous Zeno's Dichotomy Paradox. Trying to apply infinite divisibility to a finite space (of time, here) creates apparent paradoxes that aren't so easily resolved.

Here, then, I wish to make a big point about infinity again: from my perspective, all of these abstractions are indicative of the map, not the terrain. We seek to understand the world using our own logical map, since it is the only way we can make sense of the terrain, but reality is not dependent upon our map—it's quite the other way around. Because of this, I fully expect that whatever solution to Zeno's Dichotomy Paradox is eventually accepted, if one ever is, it will have been given by physicists or philosophers deeply informed by physics, not by any argument about abstractions disconnected from but weirdly applied to reality.

Dot, Dot, Dot

7

Are there perfect circles?

The question of whether or not there can be perfect circles in reality, or even in our imaginations, is meant to highlight how unsettling it might be for us to accept the idea that actual infinities are not a reality. If they are not, then a consequence is that we also do not have perfect circles, even if our approximations could be outstandingly good. It is essentially an aside, included to give a sense of how unsettling rejecting infinity outright is.

. . .

As I have mentioned, there isn't any evidence that there are what are known as real, physical manifestations of the infinite, meaning physical, real-world collections that are infinitely numerous. We have no meaningful way to construct them from finite collections, and yet we have no automatic reason to believe that the universe itself is finite in scope, even if the observable universe necessarily is and always will be, a fact predicated upon a finite speed of information transfer. It is important to note, then, that this question of both physical and actual infinities remains open.

If there are no actual infinities, and thus no physical ones, though, there are some interesting and surprising consequences. One such consequence is that without actual infinities, there cannot be real-world perfect circles (or spheres, or many other geometric figures). This is because without actual infinites, we cannot have actual measurements given by irrational numbers, which have an infinite number of decimal places and cannot be represented as a fraction of integers. As incredible as it sounds, one implication here is that necessarily, however careful we are in drawing one, no circle we can draw can actually be perfectly round. This surprising fact follows since the ratio of a circle's circumference to its diameter, π, is irrational, and thus at least one of the circumference or diameter of the circle has to be irrational in length as well. Indeed, we may not even be able to *imagine* a perfect circle, even if we can easily describe what one would be in the conceptual abstract.

If we think of actual physical objects, this isn't as upsetting as it seems at first. Real physical objects, including drawings, are made of atoms. Even if we ignore the two-dimensional circle versus three-dimensional nature problem, this ultimately means that the closest our circles can be to perfectly round is to be roughly a regular polygon with one side per atom along the drawn circumference. No doubt, this is many, many, many sides, and the result is very *nearly* a circle, but in the end, it isn't a circle.

A better example in our three-dimensional would be spheres. There are no perfect spheres if there are no actual infinities. When scientists and engineers built the highly sophisticated instrument known as Gravity Probe B, used to test predictions of general relativity, they built a gyroscope using the most perfect spheres ever manufactured. These differed from being "perfect" spheres by some forty layers of atoms here or there. In fact, they were so round that if the ping pong ball sized gyroscopes were blown up to the size of the Earth, the variation from the highest point to the lowest would have been only about eight feet difference in height. Compare this to the fact that the Earth, with its high mountains and deep ocean trenches almost fifteen miles different in elevation, if shrunk to the size of a marble, would be far smoother than the smoothest glass marble ever made.

Even so, these gyroscopes are far from perfect. Even had the engineers been able to make the gyroscopes so that there were no variations in thickness at the atomic level, blowing this object up until the atoms were the size of grapefruits or basketballs would be likely to reveal considerable irregularities from spherical perfection.

Even if we were able to leave the physical limitations of atoms behind, and indeed even if we were to be able to leave behind the limitation of the smallest scale we may be able to know—the Planck length—if there are no actual infinities, that implies that there is no infinite divisibility, which in turn implies that there are no perfect spheres or circles because the circumferences of perfectly round things *must* be an irrational constant times their diameters. In principle, anything we end up with could be blown up sufficiently many times over to reveal discontinuity in curvature. Without actual infinities, there simply aren't perfect geometric figures whose ratios of measurements depend upon irrational constants.

But this idea seems patently uncomfortable, and in terms of doing accurate mathematics, it is wildly cumbersome. Indeed, for the purpose of doing mathematics, it is vastly simpler to assume that there are infinite sets, and effectively every mathematician outside a narrow fringe does so. It is likely to be uncontroversial to point out that for typical and straightforward purposes, even many of the ultrafinitist mathematicians accept the axiom of infinity as a useful tool, even if cringing a bit about it.

Therefore, we can see that it is a simplifying assumption to accept the axiom of infinity, whether or not it accurately describes the world. It is a tool by which we create abstract models of the world, which themselves are not the world but are extremely useful for describing it. Accepting this axiom introduces infinity as an abstract quantitative notion, and doing so is enormously useful. As we repeatedly must remind ourselves, though, accepting an axiom for our model has no bearing whatsoever on the nature of reality, not any more than would drawing a tree on a map cause one to appear suddenly in the represented location.

Here, then, Platonism plays into the story. Platonic thought, in this context, essentially wrestles with the question of the meaning of existence in reality and in abstract. Plato held that the physical is just a gross representation of the perfect abstract—perfect circles certainly "exist" in the realm of ideal forms. Further, these abstractions are given a sort of numinous existence. That the mental and abstract have enormous overlaps with the numinous is a problem. As someone who rejects Platonism, I do not accept the idea that abstract existence implies real existence in any sense, and I go on to think that conflating the abstract and the real, often via the numinous, is one of the central problems that philosophical theism cannot get beyond.

It is clearly insufficient for theism, for instance, to say that "God" is nothing but the abstracted perfection of goodness, the ideal of all ideals, but this idea is the core of the philosopher's God and thus of the philosophical apologist's "God." My claim here is that "God" is an abstract notion, not a real one, and whatever real-world utility that idea has, it certainly is not an active agent that causes or does things in the universe. The "God" that we often hear about is a conflation of the abstract with the numinous, the numinous with the real, and then a personification of the ideal on top of that.

To be fair, the existence or lack of existence of actual infinities does not necessarily bear upon the existence of "God," unless "God" is given properties of infinite scope and actual infinities do not exist, but it serves as a very useful analogy into the way we can easily take the abstract and conflate it with the real, often via the numinous.

Can we say an abstraction called "God" exists, then? Perhaps we can, depending upon how the term "God" is defined. Indeed, I would argue that such an abstraction can be defined saliently. But we cannot conclude that "God" exists as a real agent, upon which the wide majority of religious belief is based, without physical evidence of it, and this conflation of the abstract and the actual is the source of many highly consequential errors. I'd also advise against calling such an abstract thing by the name "God," since people will certainly be confused by it due to more common uses of the term.

Given that the rejection of actual infinities prevents the existence of perfect circles, though, I'm sorely tempted to wonder how William Lane Craig and his followers would address the simple question of whether or not God can imagine or create an actually perfect circle.

Dot, Dot, Dot

8

From the Far Side of Infinity

What if we could look at infinity from the other side? Unsurprisingly, what we see is both weird and paradoxical. Hopefully this exploration will clarify some sense of what it means for infinity to be a "strong limit cardinal."

• • •

In Chapter 3, I introduced a concept known as a "strong limit cardinal." The point of this chapter is to explore that concept from another direction. Specifically, now we'll start at infinity and look at the matter from the other perspective.

Imagine that we have an infinite collection, the natural numbers {1,2,3,...} being a very handy and apparently intuitive set to work with. Now suppose I want to remove half of them (skipping the interesting cases where I might just remove one or some at a time). The first weird thing we notice is that we cannot simply go up to some value and say that it is the halfway point.[13] Anywhere we choose to pick has finitely many numbers below and infinitely many above. This certainly isn't cutting the set in half. In the

---

[13]   Incidentally, the bizarre "surreal number system" does allow us to do this, but it also requires that the halfway point in question is not actually a number but rather another infinite quantity. Thus, we still couldn't "go up to" it!

usual "geometric" sense, then, we can't cut the natural numbers in half because it doesn't have a middle upon which to cut.

There is an easy way to cut out half of the natural numbers, though, which is to consider divisibility by two. If a number is divisible by two (that is, even), we'll put it over here, and if it is not (that is, odd), we'll put it over there. According to the Zermelo-Fraenkel axioms, both of these sets, the evens and the odds, are equally numerous, and so half of the natural numbers are in one set and another half are in the other. So, we've cut the natural numbers in half—or have we? Those same axioms provide that we have in each of these two sets infinitely many values. Indeed, we have exactly the same number as we had in all of the natural numbers, countable infinity, so this is not half as many. This is weird.

For the argument I want to present, I will still call this "removing half of the natural numbers," because that really does make sense in a meaningful way described by what is called the "natural density." At any rate, this notion is intuitive enough to be getting on with for that purpose. Now, then, what do I have after removing half of the natural numbers? Well, I already said: I have the same number I started with. If I remove half of those, I still have the same number (one fourth of the originals now). If I remove half of those, I still have the same number (one eighth of the originals). If I remove half of those, I still have the same number (one sixteenth of the originals). No matter how many times I do this process of removing half of them, I still have the same number that I started with with successively smaller fractions identifiably present.

This means that the concept of a strong limit cardinal is really a two-sided beast. On the one hand, if I start with something finite, I cannot get to infinity by repeated successorship or exponentiation, and on the other hand, if I start with infinity, I cannot get to the finite by repeated finite removals or (negative) exponentiation. Sure, I could get to a finite set by removing everything larger than five, for example, but this is the inverse of adding infinitely many and is the exact kind of leap I'm saying is required to traverse to infinity from below. In summary, then, because countable infinity is a strong limit cardinal, one can neither reach it from below nor get out of it from above without having to jump between the two paradigms. That's pretty weird.

It may be useful to try to explore this with a physical example, in fact, to really get our intuitions going. For instance, consider what it would mean if there were a star an infinite distance away, shining its light out into space. Photons from that star would never reach us. Since the speed of light is finite, this is the successor process at work, and successors will never "get to" infinity. So, that star's light would never get here, and its mass, via gravity, would have no impact on us (or anything we can know about). In every meaningful sense, a star imagined to be infinitely far away is completely identical to a star that does not exist—at least except in our minds.

Weirder still, if I follow the ideas suggested by the surreal numbers, which *does* define fractions of countable infinity as their own mathematical objects, we could imagine another star were half as far away. (*Nota bene*: This doesn't mean anything without a structure like the surreals to define it, although our intuition kind of likes it.) Well, the same would be true

83

of it; it would still be infinitely far away, epistemically identical to not existing. If there were a third star half again as far away, the same would be true yet again. If a fourth star were half again as far away, the same thing again. In fact, no matter how many stars I define like this, be that tens, hundreds, billions, or numbers that are still every bit as embarrassingly small even if they don't feel like it (like a googolplex to the googolplex power), all are still infinitely far away (and each is infinitely far away from each other).

As this starts to sink in, the idea of an infinite universe starts to feel pretty uncomfortable. This leads me to a point that I will develop more in Chapter 10: our intuition is pretty poorly equipped to handle these questions, doing us the serious disservice of graying out the part where we jump between finite and infinite without really facing that such a chasm cannot be jumped without merely asserting it to have been done.

This brings me to God. In *God Doesn't; We Do*, I make the argument that the omni-grade (meaning infinite in scope) properties of God are haphazardly applied possibly as the result of a memetic arms race.[14] The quality of this arms race of memes can be summarized by the following exchange familiar to almost everyone who has ever been a child ever (at least in the United States):

"My God is bigger than yours!"

"Nuh uh, my God is twice as big as yours!"

"Nuh uh, my God is a hundred times as big as that!" *(Nota bene*: No child's or theist's mind I am aware of has ever noticed the recursion that breaks

---

14   See *God Doesn't; We Do* p. 67.

this game here. Specifically, if Adam's God is twice as big as Billy's God, and Billy's God is twice as big as Adam's God, then Adam's God has to be four times as big as Adam's God and yet only twice as big as Adam's God, which implies either nonsense, that God is zero, or that God is infinity, breaking the game. They also seem not to notice that making the numbers bigger doesn't really mean all that much in terms of their goals.)

"Yeah, well my God is thousand times as big as that!"

"Well, my God is a *million times* as big as that!" (Emphasis makes a million no bigger, but it doesn't preclude the behavior.)

This game tends to continue until names for bigger numbers cannot be thought of on the fly, which is another important point to make.

And then, we have it: "*My God is infinitely bigger than your God!*"

Sadly, this often continues with "infinity plus one" or "infinity times two," but we know now that this reveals a lack of understanding of infinity—and thus of the underlying God—as opposed to clarity of any sort. I suppose a savvy operator could start climbing the cardinalities of infinity, but that process is also interminable and quickly gets nonsensical. Making God infinite, then, is a profound weakness for the concept, as we will see most clearly in Chapter 16.

Here, though, there are a few points to make (other than the similarity of omni-God and characters in the *Dragonball Z* cartoon series). First, it is rhetorically very easy to make the jump to infinity, but because infinity is a strong limit cardinal, it is impossible to make this jump without just making something up. This act of creativity necessarily includes accepting the axiom of infinity, which in terms of arguments for actual deities would be question begging.

Second, as I argue in *God Doesn't; We Do*, and mentioned just above, this reveals a fundamental lack of understanding of what is going on. This is expected of children, but it is not acceptable of supposedly sophisticated adults, including those who happen to be theists (who certainly wouldn't want to commit heresy by mischaracterizing their God, right?). For instance, if God is already "really" infinite, like Catholic dogma and apologists assert, none of these claims of being so-many times as big changes the size at all, including "infinity times bigger."

Third, the jump happens precisely when we run out of names for numbers or patience with the game, *which happens infinitely long before we run out of numbers*. This strongly underscores my point that we gray out the jumps between finite and infinite specifically because eventually we just aren't good at conceiving of larger numbers (probably we actually aren't able to do so at all).

Fourth, as I also argue in *God Doesn't; We Do*, I think this memetic arms race is a necessary consequence of the definitions of "God" that people use. Each culture, religion, denomination, sect, or church merely has to argue convincingly that their God-concept is bigger and more effectively inclusive than the others, and they can win superstitious converts who don't want to be on the wrong side of a stronger, inclusive-if-you-agree deity.

As the Peano Axioms that underlie number theory essentially suggest that infinity needs to exist (as an abstraction) and yet cannot show that it actually must, a finite God never provides security against the problem of simply arguing for a bigger God. Thus, eventually, they go infinite with it, even if doing so amounts only to a rhetorical trick. That they make their deity (necessarily?) abstract in the process apparently falls between the cracks.

This status of being abstract is to be distinguished from being either physical of the diabolical "spiritual," which depends upon substance dualism. Substance dualism asserts that there are two kinds of fundamental substances, physical stuff and spiritual stuff, and it is a philosophical construction that isn't doing so well against examination in the marketplace of ideas— however well it seems to sell.

Dot, Dot, Dot

9

Mathematics Has Human Fingerprints

Mathematics is a human endeavor. Logic is a human-made tool. The number of "gotcha!" retorts asking "Well, who made mathematics?" or "Where do you think logic comes from?" I get from religious apologists is astounding, often citing the Gospel of John in the Bible. Sadly for Christians, the Bible never is and never was a reliable source about most of its claims, and its profoundly Neoplatonist idea from the Evangelist called John, that Jesus is the *Logos* made flesh, has no real grounding. In fact, we can ignore it entirely, along with the similar claim in Islam that the Qur'an is the physical embodiment of the same thing. The endeavor of mathematics really is a human thing, and I feel that this humanness is a nail in the coffin for Platonism.

• • •

Now it is time to reveal the humanness of mathematics and bring ourselves to the gate of yet another deep and unsettled debate in the philosophy of mathematics, a debate more than two millennia old. Here, I want to talk more about axioms and Platonism directly.

Recall that axioms are statements that we are unable to prove and yet that we assume the validity of in order to get started with the logical process, be it deductive or inductive. This is why I say claiming that "God" exists is an axiom, a thought reinforced by refrains from apologists asserting that "in order to get to God, we have to start with God." Of course, this kind of statement sounds an awful lot like the axiom of infinity at this point, and so my conclusion is the same. That "God" exists is an axiom, then. We can cry circular reasoning all we want, but if they want to define "God" into abstract "existence" that way, our work is mostly done. We really just have to point it out, perhaps with a fitting "So what?"

Axioms undergird the entire process of doing logical reasoning. Our usual logical framework in the West operates with two truth values: true and false. This logic is called *Boolean* logic. Others, as in some Eastern systems, have more. Some logics, the "fuzzy" ones, have infinitely many truth values.

If this sounds like a rather manufactured endeavor, it's because it is. Indeed, my position is that it's entirely manufactured—that reality, including our evolution, has determined our methods of doing logic and not the other way around. Platonists think otherwise, though. I think it is important to let our abstractions be abstract without the requirement to believe that they lay the foundation for or actually exist in reality.

It's easy, if not a Platonist, to reject the Platonic position as being rather silly. That our axioms fit reality so well and thus produce such effective mathematical and scientific models, though, makes rejecting it properly more difficult, and, as noted, Platonism is a seductive idea. We often forget, though, that we choose our axioms, thus our axiomatic systems, and we don't just choose them willy-nilly (perhaps unless we're theologians).

For the Platonist, this leaves open the argument that the ideals are out there, and we attempt to find them by choosing our axioms. The issues that arise around the edges, for committed Platonists, are a result of failing to choose our axioms perfectly, instead employing crude approximations and erroneous guesses that cause the problems, usually paradoxes. A non-Platonist, perhaps someone who asserts that abstractions are a certain kind of fiction, would contend that we're creating these ideas as we go along, doing the best we can with them.

As if to settle the debate, recall that in 1940, a logician named Kurt Gödel proved his famous Incompleteness Theorems. These lead us to see that humanness plays a clear role in the process of developing our maps and models. In fact, for many purposes, we see that we have to make intentional choices about which axiomatic systems we want to use for various purposes. It is very tempting, then, to think, "hey, wait a minute... doesn't Gödel's work kind of cast some doubt on the Platonist position?" Well, it can be read that way—in fact, I read it that way—but to really complicate this messy affair, Gödel himself was a Platonist.

If we want to start looking at the edges of our frameworks, infinity is a great place to start. Indeed, infinity isn't just an example of this problem at play—it really is *the* example. Infinity is the seam where the abstract really tears free from reality, either sooner or later. Dating into antiquity, debates about the infinite (and their inverses, infinitesimals) have been a major issue in the philosophy of mathematics. Archimedes rejected infinity outright, and so we call the rejection of the infinite (itself an axiom) the *Archimedean Principle*. Others developed complex and intractable notions about it, given the mathematical machinery of the day. It took another until the twentieth century to start to "shed light" on this problem, but that's rather the exact opposite of what happened.

To see what I mean, we have to remind ourselves about Peano and his axioms, as we discussed in Chapter 3. These axioms, in and of themselves, are not terribly controversial and appeal to reality very nicely: zero is a number, equals means what equals means, etc., and that the successor (add one) of any number is also a number. With them, we defined number theory, an important element in mathematics, and started wondering about infinity. The problem, unknown to Peano, is that his axioms themselves cannot tell us what to do about infinity, and so we are left with some choices to make about the existence of infinity.

As it turns out, the choices we have seem to complicate things. In our attempt to handle that the Peano Axioms predict infinite quantities but do not allow us to define an infinite set, we have at least four choices concerning infinity and the Peano Axioms.

1. We can accept the axiom of infinity, and with some work, number theory can be rewritten in terms of the set theory, Zermelo-Fraenkel, that resulted from doing so.

2. We can accept the negation of the axiom of infinity (that is, reject the axiom), which may lead us to finitism or ultrafinitism but leaves us with unanswerable questions about infinity.

3. We can chalk up the question of the axiom of infinity to "incompleteness," leaving it unanswered and unanswerable. That is, we can accept the Peano Axioms as they are without adding more axioms to it, at the cost of being unable to answer very intuitive and natural questions—like what it means that the set of

counting numbers appears to be an infinite collection.

4. We can use it to decide that the Peano axiomatic system is inherently flawed and start over.

I would suggest that some contemporary mathematicians would say that it doesn't particularly matter which path we choose, since nothing prevents us from following all of them to see what they're worth, but Platonists cannot accept this. Platonists essentially believe that there is a correct logic, *Logos*, and our endeavors in these veins are seeking to discover what it is. For the Platonist, one or more of the above choices, since they have some overlap, is the *right* choice. Critically worth noting, there are viable options for how to interpret mathematics because of these sorts of choices, and Platonists are trapped into thinking that only one of those choices can be correct.

Let us now suppose that we do as mathematicians did following Cantor's work and reformulate the axioms that underlie mainstream mathematics according to choice (1), which really, in practice, was choice (4) since it sought to build number theory from set theory and not the other way around. The Zermelo-Fraenkel axioms (ZF) resulted, and as Gödel would later be able to explain, the same problem arose on another unanswerable question, the question about the "continuum hypothesis."

Since it relates to infinity, we need a short aside about the continuum hypothesis: The acceptance of ZF set theory, and with it at least one infinite set, implies that there isn't just one size of infinite (requiring a more sophisticated definition of "infinite" than "not finite"). Indeed, there are infinitely many sizes of infinity under ZF! A natural question, then, is "which infinity tells us how many infinities there are?" An important generalization of the continuum hypothesis essentially posits that the first infinity, the number of natural numbers, is the number of infinities. No one can prove that, though, from within ZF, although there exist a large number of statements that are equivalent to it, including the axiom of choice. Recall that the axiom of choice states, to be very loose, that it is possible to select one object from each of infinitely many non-empty bins containing indistinguishable objects.

Hence, as before, at this point we get to make another choice with at least four possibilities:

1. Accept the axiom of choice into ZF, which gives us the system ZFC, the most commonly used axiomatic system in modern set-theoretic mathematics—though it has issues on the abstract frontier.

2. Explicitly reject the axiom of choice, maintaining ZF, which gives us the system ZF~C (read: ZF, not C).

3. Leave it alone, carrying on with ZF and leaving the question about C undecided (which actually speaks to how I was actually taught mathematics at the post-graduate level, with the proviso that many contemporary mathematicians accept choice and note explicitly that they are doing so).

4. Decide that ZF is inherently broken and reformulate from the ground up.

Secretly, there's a fifth option here, a variant on choice (4). It pitches first-order logic entirely in order to reformulate ZFC in what is called second-order logic. This possibility gives us what is known as the von Neumann-Bernays-Gödel system (NBG), which starts with the axiom "everything true in ZFC is true in NBG." NBG is well beyond the scope of this little book to go into any detail about.

Which one of those choices is right? As Gödel's result tells us, nothing in ZF can tell us. Most mathematicians accept ZFC, but it carries with it a couple of fairly non-intuitive and perhaps undesirable facts. These are interesting enough to delve into a little, though the terminology will get a little thick.

If we accept the axiom of choice, then it is possible to construct "non-measurable sets." An example of a non-measurable set is the Vitali set, courtesy of another eponymous Giuseppe. Without getting into the details of it, measurability is the abstract extension of the concept of being able to determine the length (of intervals) and has been the key foundation of modern analysis, which is essentially calculus all grown up. Accepting non-measurable sets is possibly problematic.

The reason it is problematic is because accepting the existence of non-measurable sets provides the famous Banach-Tarski Paradox, which says that we can take a three dimensional object like a sphere, decompose it into a finite number of non-overlapping pieces, and put those pieces back together without changing their "shapes" to yield two identical copies of the original sphere. (This would emphatically *not* be physically possible, I should note, since the pieces aren't measurable!) In our most basic understanding of mathematics, the counting of objects, then, the Banach-Tarski Paradox can be seen, in a way, as suggesting that 2=1, and that's not good. If we accept the axiom of choice, then we get the Banach-Tarski Paradox. But the axiom is useful enough in abstract math so that most mathematicians have accepted it!

How are we to tell which one of these things is the right way to go? You tell me. Especially troubling is that these kinds of questions will keep arising, so I essentially take the position that all of this is abstraction. We do it in an attempt to give us the ability to understand nature—by yet other abstractions that map our calculations and models onto what we experience. At some point, we have to embrace this all-too-human aspect of our mathematics, but absolutely nothing provided by Gödel's theorems suggests where. Some people, finitists for instance, draw the line at the axiom of infinity. Other people do not.

What the hell, then?

Yeah, exactly. For me, all of this mish-mash just suggests that whatever shape reality actually has, our axiomatic systems wrap themselves around it only slightly imperfectly, but imperfectly all the same, in our ongoing attempt to find the best approximation for understanding the world that we can have. If insights are available under one system and under another system contradictory to it (for examples, ZFC and ZF~C), we may not need be particularly fussed about it because I don't actually think ZFC or ZF~C or any other logical framework necessarily matches reality. It's like having two useful maps that show us slightly different things, in a sense.

The idea that our abstractions have a fundamental reality, especially one that underlies physical reality, lands on its face in the light of the fact that they follow from other abstractions, called axioms, that we choose. Of course, we do not choose them willy-nilly, but we choose them just the same, writing them as our best attempt at understanding the allegedly self-evident facts of nature—and apparently beyond into the abstract that may be only for its own sake. They are a map for us to understand nature within our minds, and we cannot keep making the mistake of confusing the map for the terrain.

I see this line of thinking as having a pretty big up-shot in the debate about religion, especially about Christianity. Christianity, thanks to the Gospel of John and the leanings of many of the Church Fathers (including whoever wrote the Gospel of John, appar-ently) were Platonists (more accurately, they were Neoplatonists). Christians believe that a significant aspect of their three-in-one God is the *Logos*, and the first chapter of the Gospel of John is an homage to how the *Logos* predated all but God and became flesh in Jesus. The Bible, then, claims a Platonist view, and we can see that there are distinct interpretations of reality that have very solid meaning without having to accept that view. Particularly, seeing "God" as an abstract notion instead of an aspect of reality is, to me, a good way to think about the world.

Hence, when Christians want to argue with me that logic itself proves that God exists as the giver of logic, not only am I glad to pin them to that definition of God that they've given (and cannot effectively connect to others as they need to), I'm comfortable in saying that that statement itself is on shaky philoso-phical ground. In other words, I have better reasons not to accept it than that it's a bald assertion—it's a bald assertion made against other more plausible possibilities.

Another small upshot is that, as I mentioned, it allows us to see their God, which has no credible evidence backing it, as an abstract idea. Its existence is an axiom within an axiomatic system. This makes it very difficult to see God as a being that does anything, and not least makes it appear ridiculous that the existence or success of mathematics is proof that some God must exist.

• • •

Naive Probability With Infinity
(It tricked me too)

• • •

Probabilities are, in many respects, all that matter when we discuss what we know about reality. As philosophers are quick to point out, certainty may only be available in strict, formal disciplines like mathematics and philosophy, and there, certainty is only certain against the underlying axioms. In the real world, we rely upon probabilities and live with the epistemic gaps they define. Infinity, though, being wildly unintuitive and frankly weird, sets up some pitfalls for handling probabilities. There are plenty of ways in which it is entirely sensible to employ the infinite with regard to calculating probabilities, but importantly, there are also plenty of ways to go awry. Indeed, I have to admit this fact plainly because even as a mathematician writing what I thought to be a careful argument, I fell for the deceptiveness of intuition too.

Dot, Dot, Dot

10

A Guess on Psychology and Infinity

This is an introduction to a key idea I want to talk about regarding applying infinity to probabilities: that of applying a uniform probability distribution (where every potential outcome is equally likely) to a space with infinite measure. Mainly, though, while I will introduce the mathematics, I will try to dig into the psychology of why infinity is so counterintuitive. I think that particular attempt at insight is worth at least as much as the bald fact that we cannot actually do what is so tempting—extend some of our intuitive probabilistic reasoning to infinite-measure sets.

· · ·

Something that is dear to my thought process, not least because it is related to an argument that I present in chapter five of my first book, *God Doesn't; We Do*, is the question of handling probability in spaces that contain infinitely many points. This topic can be pretty, or it can be pretty thorny and ugly, and there are many places where it gets very weird. More importantly, parts of this topic are far from settled in the field of the philosophy of mathematics, a property shared with the philosophical interpretations of probabilities. Some of these are among the bitterest debates in the philosophy of mathematics at present, being intense enough to have boiled over into the philosophy of science and the broader philosophical field of ontology.

I don't intend (and am not qualified) to venture deeply into those debates, but I do want to talk about the issue some since it is a highly seductive area to play with. It is also one in which our intuition is likely to lead us like the siren's song directly onto the rocks of nonsense. Throughout this and the next few chapters, we will need to understand something of what happens when what we call "probability density functions" are put on unbounded, infinite spaces.

A *probability density function* is a rule that tells us how we will assign probabilities to the set of outcomes we are interested in investigating, called the *sample space*. Probability density functions must satisfy a few properties, most importantly that the probabilities that they assign must be between zero, indicating no chance, and one, indicating certainty. On the grounds that *something* must happen if we do an experiment, we say that the *total probability* of the sample space must be one. That means that if we add up all of the probabilities of the mutually exclusive events within a sample space, the sum must come out to one.

Some sample spaces are finitely big, like the set of possibilities when rolling a six-sided die, which contains six outcomes. Other sample spaces are infinitely big, like the range of possible values between zero and one on the real number line, or all of the natural numbers, $\{1,2,3,...\}$. Other sample spaces are finitely big in reality but contain such a large number of possible outcomes as to be modeled approximately with infinite sample spaces, like the range of all of the heights of all living human beings. The probability density function (PDF) is what tells us the rule that assigns probabilities to various outcomes or ranges of outcomes in these sample spaces, those probabilities telling us how likely the occurrence of the relevant outcomes is.

In the case of the six-sided die, matters are relatively simple. If we assume a standard die (numbered 1, 2, 3, 4, 5, and 6, with one numeral on each face) that is fair (each outcome equally likely to occur in any roll of the die), then the PDF assigns a probability of one sixth to each of those outcomes. This kind of PDF, where every outcome has the same likelihood of occurrence, is called a *uniform* PDF on the sample space {1,2,3,4,5,6}. Since the total probability of any probability space has to be one, with six equally likely outcomes, each gets a chance of one sixth, which makes intuitive sense if we read it instead as "a one-in-six chance."

It is worth mentioning that there are different ways to interpret what this probability of one sixth means. The *frequentist* approach argues that this is meaningful because if we roll the die a very large number of times, we will get close to one sixth of the total number of outcomes showing each individual value. The *propensitist* approach argues instead that this is meaningful because there are six equally likely faces dividing up a total probability of one, taking a more theoretical tack. The famous Law of Large Numbers connects the two approaches without resolving the debate. There are still other interpretations that I will leave out of the present discussion, as my goal with mentioning it is merely to have given a taste of the unsettled nature of these questions in mathematical philosophy.

In the case of the values in the interval ranging from zero to one on the real line (denoted [0,1] if we include zero and one), we cannot define the uniform

PDF by saying that it gives an equal chance of picking any value. This is a consequence of the fact that there are uncountably infinitely many outcomes in that interval, and so the chance of picking any particular value is zero, almost surely, which tells us nothing about the PDF (since it is true for any PDF we could put on [0,1]). Instead of worrying about the chance of picking a particular point, we shift our attention to the chance that the point we pick will turn up in a given range of values. A uniform PDF in this case assigns the same chance to all ranges of equal size. Perhaps the most straightforward way to handle this problem is by using calculus, specifically, the integral. Fortunately, because this case is simple enough, we only need basic geometry to discuss it, though.

Here, the uniform PDF on [0,1] is given by the horizontal line at height one above the interval [0,1]. In the continuous case, we say that the probability that a value is in some range of values is given by the area of the region under the PDF. Here, say we want to find the probability that a randomly selected point will occur within the interval $[a,b]$ within [0,1]. Then this amounts to finding the area of the rectangle below the line at height one, above the horizontal axis, and between the endpoints of the specified interval, a and b. In this example, this is a rectangle with height one and width b-a. A more specific example might be if we choose a=1/4 and b=3/4, then we get that the probability that a uniformly distributed random selection from [0,1] will occur in [1/4,3/4] is one half because the rectangle formed by those boundaries has height one and width one half.

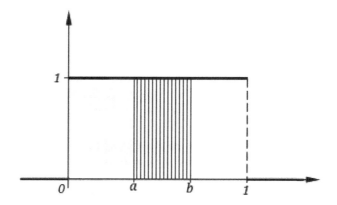

An important observation to make in this "continu-ous" case is that the mechanics are completely different. In the "discrete" case, like the six outcomes on a die, we can add together all of the individual probabilities, that's six one-sixths, to get the total probability of one. In the continuous case, it only kind of works like this—with calculus bridging the gap. Instead of adding together each value, we lump together ranges of values, in a sense, and then add those together, with calculus being the tool that lets us imagine that the ranges we're lumping together can be treated as being as small as we want.

Particularly, this difference in mechanics is high-lighted by thinking about what happens if we remove a single value under consideration. In the case of the die, if we pretend six is no longer a possibility, then we only have five possible outcomes. We've changed the cardinality of the sample space from six to five. On the other hand, if we remove a single value from the interval [0,1], we will not remove enough possibilities to change the size of the sample space. In the continuous case, we don't change the length at all by removing a point since the "length" of individual points is zero. Strange though this sounds, points are zero-dimensional and thus have no length by definition.

The mechanics in the continuous case should raise an eyebrow for us when we look at it closely. The total probability of the space has to be one, but the probability of each individual outcome in the continuous case is zero. Thus, in the continuous case, looking at it this way tells us that we are somehow adding up a whole bunch of zeroes to get one! We get out of this problem by noting another property that all probabilities must satisfy (even in the most abstract sense); they are by definition only *countably additive*.

What "countable additivity" means is that our usual rules of addition only apply for a countable infinity of values or fewer. In the continuous case, since we have *uncountably* infinitely many values added together, the usual rules of addition don't apply! Thus, we get the very odd and slightly uncomfortable idea that modern mathematics indicates (for good reasons, valid at least against the underlying axioms) that if we add up enough zeroes, where "enough" has to be certain kinds of infinite, we can get something that isn't zero! Admittedly, that's pretty weird. Indeed, if we think carefully enough about this, it leads us to another important collection of points about infinity and probability, which I call Exhibit A, developed at the end of the chapter.

Now, to make a brief aside, if we go far enough into the "large number" discrete cases, we can make a solid argument for using the continuous case as an approximation—even if we accept the ultrafinitist position that infinity, and thus continua, do not really exist. In the case of the range of potential human heights, for example, we have a sample space at least as big as the range between the smallest baby and tallest conceivable adult, a range a few thousand outcomes broad at the centimeter scale and a few tens of thousands broad at the millimeter scale. We could treat this discretely, trying to find out the rough probability of each possible height, say in millimeters, but it can be easily approximated with a continuous PDF as well. Of course, the PDF for actual heights is not really continuous, but the approximation is close and very handy, giving some practical justification for using infinity even if it doesn't exist in actuality. Of note, this PDF is an example of one that is *not* uniform—values near the average height are more likely than ones near the extremes.

So when does this get weird? Well, consider the case of the full set of natural numbers. I offer this example in *God Doesn't; We Do* to appeal to intuition, and by doing so, I listened to the siren song too much and committed a minor error. The song is so sweet that even a mathematician can fall prey to it!

The example I wanted to follow considers selecting a random number from various intervals of whole numbers that keep getting bigger: say, between one and six, between one and ten, one and one hundred, one and one million, one and one billion, and so on. If we assume a uniform distribution in each case, we see probabilities of selecting some special number—say one, which is in all of the collections mentioned—as being 1/6, then 1/10, then 1/100, then 1/1,000,000, then 1/1,000,000,000. These numbers are getting smaller and smaller and smaller as we make the sample space bigger and bigger and bigger.

107

The implication that follows our intuition is easy. What if we go all the way to infinity? Well, we get probability zero for drawing one from all of the natural numbers with a uniform distribution on them, right? No.

The problem is that even though we have infinitely many zeroes added together here, we don't have enough to break the usual rules of addition. The natural numbers are countably infinite, and countable additivity says that the usual rules of addition apply. So, if we try to add up all those zeroes, one for every natural number, we don't actually have enough of them to get a nonzero number. Thus, we get zero for the total probability of the whole space, but the total probability for the whole space has to be one. This is a problem, and what it tells us is that the probability of each individual natural number, if uniformly distributed, cannot be zero.

On the other hand, if we say the probability of selecting each number is anything nonzero, maintaining that the probabilities are all equal to one another, then the sum of all of those values, no matter how small they each are, is infinite, not one. The usual rules of addition tell us that adding up infinitely many equal nonzero values, no matter what they are, will give us infinity. Our choices, then, if we want to put a uniform probability on the whole set of natural numbers, is that the total probability has to be either zero or infinity, neither of which is one. This fails the definition of a probability, then. Hence, we cannot put the uniform PDF on the set of natural numbers, and the reason is that PDF cannot exist because it is logically contradictory.

But it feels so natural.... I don't refer to the desire to put a uniform probability on the set of natural numbers as a siren's song for nothing! Our intuition makes us expect that the uniform distribution makes sense here, but it doesn't. So what gives?

What gives is that we can't think about infinity the way we intuitively want to. To motivate the necessary discussion, I want to address a very common misconception people have when thinking about this topic. Many people think that the absence of the possibility of a uniform distribution on the full set of natural numbers would mean that it is somehow impossible to choose at random from amongst all natural numbers. This is also incorrect. It's just that the PDF that describes how likely elements are to be chosen cannot be uniform. We have to use a PDF that assigns different probability values to different numbers, and so when we say "choose a number at random from amongst all natural numbers," that is automatically and necessarily what we mean, even if we don't mean to mean it. The PDF we choose must be such that if we add up all of the probabilities for every number, we get one.

One example of a non-uniform distribution on the natural numbers has already sneakily been given. Consider the PDF that assigns a probability of one sixth to each of the numbers 1, 2, 3, 4, 5, and 6. Now extend the PDF to all of the natural numbers by saying it also assigns the value zero for every number bigger than six. This is the same PDF we had for a fair six-sided die, now extended to the infinite space of all natural numbers, and it is a valid PDF on the set of natural numbers, though on this bigger set it is not uniform. Particularly, notice that not every number is equally likely to occur because, for example, seven is less likely than six is. We avoided trouble by assigning a probability of zero to an infinite number of possible outcomes, all values larger than six.

We aren't stuck having to assign probability zero to infinitely many natural numbers to get a valid PDF, though. In fact, we aren't forced to assign a probability of zero to *any* natural number. For example, if we consider the PDF that assigns probability "one half to the n power" to the number n for every natural number, then the probability that we would select one is one half, that we'd get two is one fourth, that we'd get three is one eighth, and so on. This rule works as a PDF because the infinite sum over all values of n is one! Here, not every number is equally likely to occur, clearly, so again, the PDF is not uniform.

In wanting for a uniform PDF on the natural numbers, some people argue that it is absurd to imagine that such a PDF is logically invalid. They ask us to imagine a situation in which we have a bag with an infinite number of labeled balls in it, one for each natural number. We could shake them up and then reach in to select one at random, so their case goes, and so that would mean that there must be a uniform PDF on the natural numbers, right? Nope. It doesn't get around the problem. The problems with this bag are copious and will be discussed in a few moments.

Some others want to argue that we can define a very small thing called an "infinitesimal," small the way infinity is large. These are defined, in fact, to be so small that they are no longer actually positive, although bigger than zero. Infinitesimals are the reciprocals of infinities, and there are entire fields of mathematics that have developed (and that are still developing) to try to describe and work with them. There are problems with this approach too, and they do not satisfactorily get us away from the problems with assigning a uniform PDF to the natural numbers. See what I've called Exhibit A at the bottom of this chapter for more information.

Why is it so alluring then? What gives?

Well, I suspect that because (countable) infinity is a strong limit cardinal, we are actually not very good at conceiving of what infinity really means. Indeed, since all of our usual attempts to conceive of infinity quantitatively are of the constructive type, using something like succession or exponentiation to try to make our concept grow "toward infinity," we are falling for the idea that we can "get to" infinity when indeed, we cannot. That's the meaning of it being a strong limit cardinal. To "get there," we have to cheat and just jump there.

Our intuition doesn't work that way, though. It says, "ten things, yeah, okay; one hundred; yeah; a million, no problem; you can see where this is going." Then it cheats and makes the jump. The thing is, by using this method, we will never get there. Add one more? Always finite. Put another zero on the end? Still finite. Double the number of digits? Still finite every. single. time. Our intuition, though, simply isn't so careful, and it just hops over the three-dot ellipsis, ignoring where all of the infinity is.

Rephrasing this intuition in terms of probabilities, our intuition will tell us "one in ten, yeah, okay; one in a hundred, yeah; one in a million, no problem; you can see where this is going." Then our intuition cheats us and makes the jump. The problem is, it jumps to something that isn't there, but our intuition is too stupid or too ill-equipped to realize that truth—often even when we know better.

That means that when we're doing the "you can see where this is going" step, our intuition is pulling a fast

111

one on us by thinking of successively lower and longer PDFs that may look similar to the case with the fair die, and then it suddenly jumps. When it jumps is when we punt on not being able to really fathom the numbers any longer. In making this jump, what it doesn't realize that it has done is to have assigned a "tail behavior" to most of the remaining values above some arbitrary "large" number—maybe it's the googolplex or the googolplex raised to the googolplex power; it really doesn't matter. That is, our intuition inherently builds a PDF that either drops off to zero at some point and ever after, or it trails off to zero fast enough after some point so that the total sum of the probabilities of every possible outcome is still one. In doing so, most of the natural numbers are implicitly assigned a probability much lower than the numbers we can imagine. Importantly, it does this without us realizing it.

That brings us back to that bag example. The bag with infinitely many labeled balls in it has some issues with it. First, how did infinitely many balls all get into the bag in the first place? This isn't just a matter of real-world practicality or philosophical pedantry. If added sequentially or even in ever-growing (but still finite) lumps, the bag will never be filled. The only way around this, without cheating and just saying infinitely many balls are in there as a brute fact about the bag, is to add balls so fast that the time intervals converge, as with Thomson's lamp. That, though, becomes utterly ridiculous at some point.

If we do suppose that we somehow magically have that bag full of infinitely many balls, we still have a problem, though. The discussion above really reveals what it is: we know the PDF cannot be uniform, and so we have to conclude that it cannot be possible to assign equal probability to every ball in the bag. Even

112

though the bag example is given to overcome this problem, the issues at its heart make a lot of sense as soon as we imagine such a thing.

For instance, this bag presumably is meant to be reached into in order to pick a ball. That makes us imagine its dimensions. If it is only finitely big around, then it must be infinitely deep. At some point, I think we all have to admit that the balls way down in there (there can be no bottom, actually) are less likely to be chosen than the balls nearer the top. This is where our intuition does the jumping thing. Down to any specified depth, we're good to go and can force the analogy for our uniform PDF. The problem is that infinitely many balls are below that specified depth, and our intuition automatically either ignores almost all of those balls, or it implicitly assigns a diminishing significance to their role in the problem and thus a shrinking likelihood of choosing them. In this case, then, by forcing a PDF onto the whole set of natural numbers, we see it is not uniform.

On the other hand, if the bag is infinitely big around, then although we may or may not have a bottom to the bag, the bag has no edges. We do the same kind of fuzzing out around *imagined* edges in this case, ignoring vast swaths of balls (almost all of them, in fact) outside certain imagined edges—the ones that defy our intuition. Yet again, the forced PDF is not uniform.

Thus, imagining a bag that forces us to envision a random selection from the whole set of natural numbers also forces a non-uniform PDF to the balls in it. Once we realize that, the reasons start to seem pretty obvious; such a bag even in principle forces us to ignore most of the balls in it. Our intuition doesn't realize it, but it is so.

113

In general, then, bag analogy or not, the reason I suspect we feel like it is intuitive to do the impossible and put a uniform PDF on a space with infinite measure comes down to our having to ignore the vast majority of the values that comprise the infinite. We do this when we ultimately cheat and jump the gap to the strong limit cardinal that is infinity. Our ignorance of the majority of the values is so complete that we are too ignorant to realize we're ignoring them, and them is almost all of them.

Exhibit A

A savvy reader will have noticed when discussing the continuous case, we get nonzero probabilities by the uncomfortable (and weird) notion that we add up sufficiently many zeroes. This raises interesting questions about infinitesimals, the reciprocals of infinities. They aren't intuitive objects either, as it turns out.

Recall that this question arose both for the whole interval $[0,1]$ and the smaller interval inside it, $[a,b]$. This observation should strike us as even more weird, then, when we are made aware of the fact that the number of values in $[0,1]$ and in $[a,b]$ is exactly the same. Indeed, it's the same as all of the numbers on the entire real line, stretching to every positive and negative value with a decimal representation. Thus, by adding together the same number of sufficiently many zeroes, we can get any finite value (the lengths of finite intervals) and infinity (the whole real line). Indeed, we can even get zero, but not by considering true intervals (an example being what is called the Cantor Set).

This is a major point that underscores the frustrations involved in attempting to use infinitesimals to get around the problem at the center of this chapter, that uniform PDFs cannot be put on spaces of infinite measure. That point is that we cannot know what result we should get by adding together a given number of infinitesimals. In the continuous case discussed here, we saw that adding uncountably infinitely many zeroes gave us one for one interval and gave us b-a (=1/2 in the example I used) for another. Those aren't the same, but we added together exactly the same number of infinitesimals of exactly the same kind to get both values.

Another good example of this issue occurs when we look at the natural numbers. As discussed, it is very intuitive to want to say that the probability of picking an even number from the naturals (with a hypothetical uniform distribution) would be one half and that the probability of picking a number divisible by three would be one third. Indeed, attempts to make this work like brilliant mathematician Paul Erdös' *natural density* approach have chased this intuition for a long time.

Here's the problem, though. The number of even natural numbers is the same as the number of natural numbers divisible by three is the same as the number of natural numbers overall. So if I have that many infinitesimals of the kind reciprocating countable infinity and add them up, how can I distinguish between getting one third, one half, and one—or any other value—as the answer?

More frustrating for such an attempt, the natural density of the set of primes is zero, so starting from countably many countable infinitesimals, how do we know we don't get a sum of zero? Alternatively, counting all of the natural numbers against the primes, how can we know we don't get a sum of infinity? The usual way to sneak out of this is to say that we define the infinitesimal so that adding the right infinity of them together gives us one, but then we cannot account for the one half or the one third we want in those other cases. Choosing to let them add to one is an *ad hoc* way to try to get around the lack of uniform PDF on the whole set of natural numbers.

Fortunately, the example of the infinitely broad (no edges) magical bag containing balls labeled with all of the natural numbers can help clarify this point. It makes a great visual example of the preceding paragraph to imagine two different infinitely broad bags with the balls arranged into different numbers of layers. Since the bag is infinitely broad, one layer could contain all of the balls, but two layers contains just as many—not more—as do three, four, five, and, indeed, even infinitely many such layers.

It could be argued that it doesn't matter how may layers are present, but that merely dodges facing the issue for infinitesimal mathematics. If I had two identical bags of this kind, for instance, except that one contains the balls in one layer and the other has four identical layers, intuition tells us that the probability of drawing any particular ball from the four-layer bag should be one fourth of that of drawing it from the one-layer bag—but it isn't. In each bag, there is still only one ball for each natural number.

I consider this to be quite important to anyone who wants to be cautious enough to get their arguments involving infinity right. It is also important for Platonists to consider, given that their notion that mathematical objects are somehow real is severely challenged by these ideas. Further, I suppose it's worth noting that even God, if such a being existed, couldn't assign equal likelihood to all of the natural numbers, which raises some uncomfortable questions about his omniscience and omnipotence.

Dot, Dot, Dot

11

We Can't Even Force
the Impossible

Here, I'll elaborate more upon the thinking presented just previously. I'd like to illustrate what happens if we attempt to force the impossible, making this a rather meta-mathematical exploration. Of course, we can engage in thought-experiments like this specifically because these are abstractions we're examining, not physical realities. As we might expect, things tend to get weird. The results highlight some important thoughts to keep in the back of our minds while playing with the infinite and naïve attempts at doing probability.

• • •

Things get odd and absurd if we attempt to force the impossible. It makes for an interesting exploration to wonder what would happen if we tried to force a uniform PDF onto a space with infinite measure. Doing so is cheating, but for the stated purpose it is sort of justified cheating because it's an idea some mathematicians chase after and that many people inadvertently misuse. Somewhat sophisticated, if fringe, nonstandard methods of dealing with the relevant branch of mathematics (analysis) have developed a mathematics of infinitesimals that hopes to deal with it, but it only kind of succeeds, as the end of the previous chapter exposed. Because of this Holy Grail-like quality, forcing the situation isn't too out of bounds for a

119

philosophical exploration. (And yes, the allusion to the Holy Grail is meant to include its likely nonexistence.)

Suppose we use the example of the natural numbers, for relative ease and intuitive appeal. The natural numbers, again, is the set of numbers {1,2,3,...}. What we want to do is explore the situation in which we choose from this set of infinitely many numbers at random with the assumption that each natural number is equally likely to turn up in our selection. Since we can't do this, really, we'll be forcing the situation, say using infinitesimals if needed.

To get a toehold on this issue, we are going to explore a question: "What is the probability that our randomly selected number will appear in the interval (n,∞), meaning the set of all natural numbers larger than some arbitrary, but specified, number n?" To answer that question, recall that every number is smaller than most. That is, only finitely many are smaller and still positive while infinitely many are bigger than any number we consider. That gives us a chance that looks like n/∞, which is usually interpreted as zero, for picking a number in the set ranging from one to n. However we measure it, then, the probability that we will pick a number within the interval (n,∞) turns out to be one—indicating certainty. This means we'll *always* choose a number bigger than our specified n in a random selection from among all natural numbers if each natural number is equally likely. Further, this is true no matter what value n takes.

Unlikely as it seems up front, this fact follows since *if* any number divided by ∞ has any meaning, it either means zero (standard mathematics) or an infinitesimal (nonstandard mathematics). The total probability has to add to one, though, and so the probability that the chosen number will occur in the interval (n,∞) is one minus either zero or an infinitesimal. One minus zero is one, indicating certainty that the chosen number is bigger than n. One minus an infinitesimal is sometimes said to be 0.999..., and that number is also one. Others will argue that one minus an infinitesimal is just that, one minus an infinitesimal, which is ever so slightly different to one, but the result is essentially the same in both cases.

Let me rephrase that in plainer language: If we try to assume that one of the natural numbers can be selected at random with an equal likelihood of occurrence for every value, the one selected will certainly be larger than an arbitrarily specified number n. And this is true for *every* natural number n.

This packs a hard punch. To get a better sense of it, let's consider what happens when we start making n bigger, looking from beneath n. To use plain language, consider the following series of questions exploring the matter: Will our selected number be smaller than one hundred? Never. Smaller than one thousand? Never. Smaller than one million? Never. Smaller than one quadrillion? Never. Smaller than the googolplex to the googolplex power? Never. It will always be bigger than all of those. We can pick literally any number we want as a benchmark. A truly random selection will definitely be bigger than that number if we force a uniform distribution onto the natural numbers.

So, under a uniform distribution on the natural numbers, a random selection is *certain* to be larger than any, and thus every, number. That means that our random selection *isn't going to be a number*. More formally, as we let n tend toward infinity, we arrive at the fact that the number we will select, whatever it is will be, with all but absolute certainty, in the "interval"

(∞,∞). Of course, (∞,∞) isn't really what we usually mean by an interval. Indeed, it is better known as the "empty set," the set that contains nothing.

What does this mean? It means if we try to force the impossible situation of picking a number from amongst all natural numbers, uniformly distributed, we will actually fail to pick a number at all! Some people reject this conclusion, arguing that we will either pick a number or we will not, and further claiming that the original premise of "pick a number" forces that option. The proper rebuttal is that the question was fallacious in the first place because the stated probability distribution doesn't exist.

Some will persist, claiming that by hypothesis we *are* picking a number, and so a number must come out. Very well. In that case, where we absolutely adhere to the idea of picking a number, we're doing so with a distribution on the natural numbers that is not uniform, whatever the protestations. The previous chapter discussed a guess at why this seems so confusing.

Some still persist. So, what if we use infinitesimals to get around this problem, as some argue? It doesn't work. Why? By exactly the same argument as above, the probability that we pick any number at all is infinitesimal in this case, and thus it is not one. Looking at the situation globally, it *seems* to make sense to use infinitesimals, but when we start asking specific questions about which numbers might turn up, we still see that none of them will. Of course, it is worth noting yet again that infinitesimals have some other serious problems associated with their employment as discussed in the "Exhibit A" at the end of the previous chapter.

What gives? Simple: We cannot put a uniform probability distribution on an infinite-measure sample space. We can't even force it. Not even if we cheat. Not even if our argument depends upon it.

This fact should highlight another facet of how incredibly large the infinite is: it is so big that we cannot claim that all the objects in a countably infinite set can be equally likely to be chosen at random. If we want equal likelihood, that means we have to limit ourselves to the finite case or leave behind the discrete (and use calculus and more advanced tools). Even in the continuous case, though, a space with infinite measure *still* cannot have a uniform PDF put onto it for essentially the same reason. In a sense, then, infinity is so big that we have no choice but to ignore essentially all of what makes up an infinite set. And people want to define their God by this notion....

Dot, Dot, Dot

12

Revisiting My Case That the Existence of God is Infinitely Unlikely

In *God Doesn't; We Do*, I made the case that the existence of God may be able to be assigned probability zero, "almost surely." I really want to make clear that my argument in that book does not hinge upon evaluating a probability. Instead, it rests on the idea that saying we *can't* assign a probability of zero to the God hypothesis is the only apparent objection to suggesting it—both in classical philosophy and in modern Bayesian reasoning. I have reservations about the claim that probability zero is philosophically indefensible because I feel that the mathematical concept of almost sureness may provide a harbor for this argument since it is not categorical denial. That comprises the center of my argument that God's existence is infinitely unlikely.

• • •

A famous sign on a London bus read, "There is probably no God. Now stop worrying and enjoy your life."

"Probably no God...," it says, but how unlikely is it?

Richard Dawkins famously put forth a Spectrum of Theistic Probabilities in his 2006 book *The God Delu-*

sion.[15] The Spectrum is a scale from one, absolute belief, to seven, absolute unbelief. He remarks that a six on this scale is identifiable as *"De facto* atheist. Very low probability, but short of zero. 'I don't know for certain but I think God is very improbable, and I live my life on the assumption that he is not there.'" Dawkins has referred to himself as a 6.9 on this scale.[16] I wanted to explore what "short of zero" means.

In *God Doesn't; We Do,* I argue that the existence of God is infinitely unlikely. This, I suggest, possibly could be handled by modern mathematical thinking by an idea known as "almost sureness," which means true off a set of "measure" zero. These terms will need definitions.

Measure is a modern mathematical term that generalizes the length of intervals and is the standard accepted basis for analysis, a field that could be called grown-up calculus. A set has *measure zero* if its total measure is zero in an extension of the same way that zero-dimensional individual points have a length of zero on the real line. We say something is *almost sure* if the measure is a probability measure (measure of the total space is one) and if that something is true everywhere except possibly on a set of outcomes that have measure zero. To avoid a long, detailed, and abstract mathematical discussion, my case is that the "very low probability" of God's purported existence need not actually be "short of zero"; it could be said to

---

15   Dawkins, Richard (2006), *The God Delusion,* New York: Bantam, p. 50.

16   "Richard Dawkins on Bill Maher," Online video clip, *YouTube.* YouTube, 11 Apr. 2008. accessed 18 Sept. 2013.

be zero, almost surely, without automatically wading into philosophically indefensible categorical denial. We might call such events "completely implausible possibilities," to turn an intuitive phrase.

My claim in *God Doesn't; We Do* is that we lack good reasons to think that the probability that God exists is different from zero, almost surely. This carries with the suggestion that Dawkins' position on his Spectrum would more accurately be 6.999... (which happens to be 7). He could claim this, I think, at least unless I were proved wrong, without any automatic loss of philosophical defensibility. Now, normally I would say I have to prove such a claim, but the point I want to clarify here is that I don't think I actually do. That, indeed, is the thrust of the argument I make in *God Doesn't; We Do*, and I want to reiterate it here with greater clarity. Technically, I should note, I made this argument against any conception of God that does things in the world, and I don't particularly need to make a case against abstract ideas called "God." Indeed, the conclusion could be phrased alternatively as "God is almost surely an abstraction" instead of "God doesn't exist, almost surely." I mean identical things with both of those phrases.

Since I accuse theologians of shifting the burden of proof (as an art form that defines their field) all the time, it would be fair to point out that it looks like that's what I'm doing here. It's not. I'll present an argument here attempting to defend that claim. To make this a bit more poignant, I will be making a parallel argument about the Force from *Star Wars*, an idea that could serve as the basis of a religion (it does, actually, but it appears to be a satire) and yet that essentially everyone considers fictional and non-existent.

127

Lest anyone feel that this is a false equivalence because of presumed "evidence" for God's existence that does not exist for the Force, bear in mind that the Force *is* the religious object of the *Star Wars* universe that can be used to explain anything that a hypothesis of God does. Indeed, the Jedi religion bears uncanny resemblance to religious Taoism and was explicitly co-opted by George Lucas to fill the role often filled by God.[17] Note, though, that the Force is not assumed to have agency, and thus it is fundamentally incompatible with God and cannot be claimed to be God under a different name. Additionally, though we know the Force originated in a modern work of fiction, we also know that belief in God originated in our ancient superstitious past, so I don't feel that this comparison is in any way ridiculous.

So, let's start big and work to small. We should all agree that it is question begging to state *a priori* that the probability that there is a God (or some specific God) is 100%. If we assume God exists from the outset, we are, by definition, begging the question. So the probability that God exists must be less than 100% to avoid philosophical indefensibility and what amounts to nothing more than a bald assertion. *Nota bene*: This assumes a position that understands probability as measurement of our state of knowledge. There are others that I am not employing here.

Now, to handle the reverse of my assertion, could someone argue that the probability that God does exist is 100%, *almost surely*? Well, yes, but not without problems. In fact, the bulk of my case here, despite the

---

17   Silberman, Steve, "Life After Darth," *Wired*, May 2005.

detail given to other potential values for the plausibility for God's existence, arises from noting that the two almost-sure positions are the only ones we are likely to be able to make in a philosophically defensible way. I want to point out that without almost surely un-equivocal evidence, we cannot defend any other guess at the plausibility of existence.

Some might argue that I set the bar too high here, wanting to claim that the question is one of how we interpret evidence, but I disagree. Indeed, there are at least two commonplace ways in which we accept evidence of this kind. For one instance, take the kind of evidence we have regarding the existence of a dairy cow when faced with one, For another, consider the overwhelming statistical evidence garnered by predict-ing and then observing outcomes of physical experiments. In the first case, it borders on insanity to deny obvious evidence like interaction with a real macroscopic object. In the second, we get statistically strong justification that something physical exists that can be described and predicted by our models, a fact not diminished by the possibilities that our models are mistaken or are themselves fictions. It should go without saying that the God hypothesis fails to consti-tute this first kind of evidence, since all such claimed interactions with the divine are inherently subjective and are experienced at the level of the brain. On the lack of predictability and failure of consistent descrip-tion front, though, we see the God hypothesis fails this second sort of evidence as well. Indeed, no one seems to ever know what God will or won't do with the kind of certainty we see in science except until *after* the fact, when it could just as easily support vast arrays of fantastic hypotheses other than God.

The center of my argument here, then, is that I don't think any plausibility claims but "God exists, almost surely" and its opposite, "God does not exist, almost surely," can be defended in this matter. Of course, I'll also make the case that "God exists, almost surely" is less tenable than the contrary. Before getting to that, though, note that this is precisely the behavior we already see in most people who are thinking clearly: believers frequently assert 100% certainty (needing almost certainty to avoid begging the question), and those who don't believe rapidly find any specific probability larger than zero, almost surely, to be cause to raise a justified skeptical eyebrow at the claim. In case there is any doubt on this last point, I'll devote a fair amount of time to it shortly.

Now, regarding the position that "God exists, almost surely" as a starting point, observe immediately that we certainly wouldn't make such an argument about the Force, and by extension any other fiction that might fill this role. Of course, someone may argue that this is because the Force, unlike a religion like Christianity, has no credible evidence going for it, but this is a product of giving Christianity credit it hasn't earned. In fact, the kind of *post hoc* interpretation of evidence to fit a God hypothesis could be repeated effectively for the Force or any other suitably vague and yet potent fictional construction. That no one has seen anyone with the ability to manipulate the Force not only ignores (also incredible) claims made by those who believe in spiritual magic powers, say associated with esoteric martial arts, but it could be dismissed simply enough by pointing out that they simply haven't met a Jedi willing to demonstrate the ability. Eastern mystics and their adherents make this exact claim *all the time* when defending their own outrageous claims, and we have no trouble dismissing what they wish to pass as "evidence" for the phenomena.

Again, the Force, here, is just a proxy that could be filled by any suitable fiction. This, in fact, is a main criticism of taking the stance that 100%, almost surely, existence is a reasonable assumption. If we open the door to one fiction, like the Force, we have to open it to every other fiction to avoid committing special pleading for a favorite—say, God. If the probability that God exists as an entity in reality is 100%, almost surely, then we open the door, for example, to saying that the probability is 100%, almost surely, that there also exists a perfect anti-God, something akin to the Cartesian Demon[18] or the character I called Irony in *God Doesn't; We Do.*[19]

Further, we should appreciate that what passes for "empirical evidence for God" is perfectly indistinguishable from finding in the world which the believer has already attributed to God, often subconsciously or as a cultural artifact. If this is really what is going on, note that it renders God as a mental abstraction by which a believer creates proxies for explanations. I'll reiterate: I have no qualms with the notion that God is a mental construction, which this fact points to, and to whatever extent such things "exist," I will grant God's existence.

---

18 See Descartes, René, *Meditations on First Philosophy, with Selections from the Objections and Replies (Cambridge Texts in the History of Philosophy)*, Ed. John Cottingham, Cambridge University Press, 1996.

19 See *God Doesn't; We Do*, Chapter 4.

This isn't done without problems, however. To do this, as religious believers essentially already do, leads directly to unresolvable theological conflicts and thus endless denominationalism. Asserting God into existence provides absolutely nothing by which such conflicts can be addressed, aside from making more competing assertions, of course. My "Irony," in fact, puts this problem in sharp relief by arguing that God is a capricious entity that confuses us about theological matters *on purpose*, including by inspiring all of these conflicting religions and interpretations. If one were to fall to evidence as an arbiter, the evidence *strongly* favors such a capricious deity over anything the religious seek to maintain since, by definition, the only consistent fact about Irony is that he seeks to equivocate upon this matter and keep us confused. If a Christian can say "God did it, almost surely," I can say, "no, it was Irony, almost surely," and we have no way to resolve this conflict. The only possible way to avoid this problem is to do what most believers tend to do already when under close scrutiny: make "God" too vague to be useful (so, really, just an abstraction). A claim, then, that God exists, almost surely, cannot be compared with its philosophical opposite, almost sure non-existence, which opens no such unresolvable doors.

Some would argue that the question leads to an unresolvable argument between theism and naturalism, but this is also incorrect. The debate is not between the existence of God and nature as competing philosophical assertions, but it is instead between "nature with God" versus "nature without God." In this light, we see that "asserting" nature into the matter is not on a level with asserting a God into it.

132

To summarize, then, while almost sure existence may be philosophically defensible, it is simultaneously both less parsimonious and more problematic a position to take than almost sure nonexistence. On the grounds of a more cautious set of underlying assumptions, then, I rest my case for almost sure nonexistence, noting that this is not the same as categorical denial. Indeed, in the next chapter, I will make the case that almost sure nonexistence mathematically could be overcome, but *only* by almost sure evidence.

To elaborate upon specific numbers in between, revealing why these aren't valid guesses, let's turn our attention to the middle: a 50% chance. This is what Dawkins calls a four on his Spectrum, and it is a state of utter agnosticism. I don't think we can honestly hold this position, though, without asking the question of how we can suspect the likelihood could be so high as 50%. We should linger on this point, then, because the idea that we don't know, or maybe can't know, between what appears to be two possibilities provides a feeling like a fifty-fifty chance could be the right value.

"It is the case, or it isn't," they say, but that need not imply equal likelihood. For instance, at any given moment, the front door of my house might be open or it might not be open, but I know from experience that in reality it most certainly is not open half of the time. There may or may not exist a cottage made of pancakes on the far side of the moon, but it's ridiculous to suggest that there are even odds that one is there. Would anyone think it is reasonable to say "because either it exists or it doesn't, there's a 50% chance that the Force is real"? I seriously hope not! Why should agnosticism about God be treated any differently?

133

My job here, though, tempting a trap as it might be, is not to make the case that there is not even a 50% chance that God exists. It's to point out that before I should entertain the idea of a 50% chance of God's existence, it is the job of the person claiming it to be able to back up that claim somehow. Certainly, for instance, if I tried to assert without backing it up that there's a 50% chance that the Force exists, I would be mocked out of the conversation. If I said that there is a 50% chance I will roll a one on my next roll of a six-sided die, you will either not believe me or want to inspect the die for some trick, like three faces showing ones or unequal weighting that loads the odds in the favor of my claim. A savvy gambler would even ask the same thing about the outcome of a coin toss, wanting to check that the coin is fair.

Thus, I think anyone wanting to claim a 50% chance for God's existence has a burden of proof to meet before we should accept that number. Indeed, I am highly skeptical of such a high value, given a look at evidence of the world. Since "God" is the hypothesis of the believer, it should be the believer's job to establish that 50% is a reasonable number, and "it is, or it isn't!" won't do it.

Fifty percent is the cognitive hurdle. The same argument applies going downward, so we can skip quickly to 5%, just to make the point. Is there a compelling argument that the number that describes the likelihood that God exists is at least 5%? Why should I believe such a number? If intellectual honesty tempts us into think maybe so, compare against the Force. Would we require a good argument to believe that there's even a 5% chance that the Force exists? I would! It is up to the believer, in either the Force or

God, to provide such an argument, and without one we simply are not required to accept the claim.

To wit, religious claims to evidence for a deity are typically rather pitiful attempts that come in a few flavors. One sort is an argument to the necessity of God to make sense of the existence of reality, but this could just as easily be done with the Force. For example, imagine an imaginary scroll of Jedi that reads along the lines of "Originally, there was but one continuous Force, unified and whole, and then the Force suddenly and of its own accord began to stir and take shapes, which manifested the myriad things that are reality." Believers may claim such a Force is identical to God, but that's easy to remedy by any litany of doctrinal nonsense, and besides simply defining their God so following debatable claims from scripture, they lack any proof of uniqueness of such a necessary creative force. Another sort of "evidence" is an appeal to an underlying Moral Law, but a second chapter of the scroll of Jedi could read, "The Force as it stirred separated into two fundamental parts, the Light Side and the Dark Side, defining that which is righteous from that which is not." A third sort is the evidence of this world, but this is accounted for by the myriad things into which the Force "stirred." Yet another are calls to miracles of God or particular special feelings or states of mind, but then, are these the droids we're looking for?

The problem with the evidential approach to defending God's existence, is simply that if there is no God, then there is no actual evidence for God, only evidence misinterpreted to that purpose. The same evidence can be misinterpreted to the purpose of the Force or to any other sufficiently broad attributional schema, and for the motivated mind, perhaps primed

135

on Mother's knee, each is equally believable and equally worthless as an explanation for the available evidence. Religious believers have only this after-the-fact, manufactured sort of evidence, exactly the kind they'd never be able to attribute to any particular dogma without having heard that dogma first. What evidence is there, then, that gives the existence of God even 5% plausibility?

A counter could be made that religious apologists like William Lane Craig successfully provide evidence for God's existence, changing this question to one of how we interpret the evidence we have. Indeed, one could go further and note that in many meetings in which Craig speaks, the audience would easily grant him 5% (indeed, far more) without blinking. The issue with this counter is one of justifying one paradigm for interpreting the evidence over another, in this case one in which the Force should be able to compete nearly on a level with theology. The paradigm, then, that religious believers assume is unquestionably less conservative than the alternative I am advocating that assumes no God without far better evidence, since that which they are trying to claim counts as "evidence" is highly controversial, at best.

To highlight that fact, consider how much of a religious apologists' time has to be tied up in arguing for possible—not necessarily plausible—ways by which the God they defend might be squared with the evidence that we have. In Craig's case, for instance, this leaves him defending the genocides of the Old Testament as objectively moral. In all cases, apologists have to provide complicated treatments to rationalize why we do not see what we expect to see on the assumptions of religious theism. The issue called the logical problem of evil, for instance, stands squarely in the

136

way of accepting many apologetic appeals to the evidence pointing to a good-for-something God instead of away from it. We shall return to this point shortly.

First, one other counter might be raised that the sciences are just as guilty as religion of fitting the evidence to particular abstract constructions called "models." I'd argue that this is precisely what scientists do, that models are abstract constructions, but that the amount of guilt here is incomparably lower. Indeed, consider an analogous situation from the sciences. Were I to invent a hypothetical subatomic particle completely unknown to the Standard Model, does anyone believe that I could go to a meeting of particle physicists and simply claim that there is at least a 5% chance that it exists? Even if I had a very elegant theoretical framework to back me up, without evidence, it is completely unlikely I'd be taken even a little bit seriously without evidence, and for good reasons! Otherwise, anyone could make up just about anything they want with a reasonable expectation of having it believed, which at the least would be an enormous waste of everyone's too-precious time. No number of clever philosophical arguments, claims that the scientists can't technically prove it doesn't exist, or odd apologetic contortions of the available evidence would get me an ounce more credence. In fact, I'd probably get far less in that case. This is as good a time as any to remind the reader of just how effective this rigorously skeptical method has proved.

If 5% isn't defensible, what about Richard Dawkins' own intellectually honest, conservative stance? He calls the position that gives a "very low probability [that God exists]" a six on his Spectrum, so let's go there. To get there we can slide down to 1% or 0.1% or 0.00001% just the same as above—although the interesting and relevant question of what a "very low probability" might be lingers. To my point, though, where is the argument saying that God's existence is at least as likely as any of these? If this feels unfair, ask again what number would we consider to be reasonable to concede as describing the chance of the real existence of the Force? Would anyone honestly accept that there's even a one in a billion chance that the Force is real without being given some coherent theoretical or evidential reason to think so? Why should the matter with God be any different?

To reiterate and defend my analogy to the Force, bear in mind that the Force is the religious object of a fictional universe that otherwise can be assumed to obey identical physical laws to ours. That which provides life, a vessel for right and wrong, the coherence of reality, etc., is all hypothetically accounted for by the Force, but it lacks agency and thus is not identical to God. Now, it could be argued that there is surely more evidence for God than for the Force, given that we know the Force is a fiction, but notice the roots of this appeal. It comes down to the idea that because we know the Force is a fiction, any evidence interpreted to support the Force is misinterpreted to do so. Easily swept under the rug here are two analogous facts. God arose in our ancient superstitious past where lines between fact and fiction literally did not exist, and if God does not exist, *there is no evidence for God at all* either, only evidence misinterpreted to fit a God-shaped hole. My central question is why we should consider it philosophically valid to presume that there is a God but no Force. Had the Force been thought of thousands of years ago and happened to dominate the cultures that became ours, in fact, it may very well have been the centerpiece of the discussion we're having here instead.

And just look at the evidence that exists that works against the claim of a loving, omnipotent, omniscient supernatural agent! How likely is it that a morally perfect being would have provided us with such barbaric scriptures, full of examples that make our moral centers recoil and apparently indistinguishable from the ravings of superstitious and brutal people? How likely that such a deity would love us and yet hide behind impenetrable epistemic distance while we suffer and toil—with the scriptures implying it wasn't always the case? How low is the "very low probability" given this issue, called the logical problem of evil?

When considering the matter, it is important not to get taken in by the exchange of a *possibility* and a *probability*, or indeed a certainty. Apologists are quick to point out that there could *possibly* be an explanation for all of the suffering of the world and then conclude that there *probably or definitely* is one in God. Indeed, this is often the best line of defense that they have, and its goal is to obscure the reality that the probability of such explanations is abysmally low.

Thus, I contend that any positive number that an apologist might give, then, requires defense or faces the completely valid question of how such a high number is justified. If I wanted to do this in mathspeak, for any small number *epsilon* greater than zero, assuming that the probability that God exists is *epislon* demands a proper and solid defense of that claim.

"But, you can't say that!" is the main defense against this point, from both theologians and philosophers alike. In rebuttal, all there really is to say, as there are no justifications for *any* positive plausibility for the God hypothesis, is "but you can't say that the probability is zero that God exists without proving it!" Well, a few responses are warranted.

First, I haven't. I said <u>every positive probability needs an argument to support it</u>. Second, actually, I might be able to say that the probability God exists is zero, so long as I qualify it with "almost surely." Since "almost surely" admits wildly unlikely possibilities, it does not run afoul of philosophical defensibility. Again, hypotheses with a plausibility of zero, almost surely, could be called "completely implausible possibilities." Third, would we really hesitate to say the same thing about the Force, that the probability that it is real is zero, almost surely? I don't think we would.

This third point raises another interesting question, though. Are we under some kind of metaphysical obligation to entertain a hypothesis about the universe—to give it a nonzero probability of validity—just because someone wrote it down? What about hypotheses no one ever writes down or even thinks of—do we give them zero plausibility, and if so, do we do it unfairly? Does every potential hypothesis deserve a nonzero plausibility? In light of ideas like the Force, or even wackier fictions, it seems more than a bit ridiculous to suggest that they do, but it may be the case, as the usual rules of Bayesian reasoning suggest. As we have discussed, though, we cannot have infinitely many *equally likely* hypotheses with nonzero plausibilities. Thus, logical coherence dictates at the least some mechanism by which we can assign lower plausibilities, *a priori*, to some kinds of hypotheses than to others. This mechanism must provide convergence of the total probability, which means that however small the plausibility of any particular hypothesis, infinitely many more must have a plausibility considerably smaller. Of course, such a mechanism also requires justification.

So, my claim is that any attempt to argue for a nonzero plausibility for the God hypothesis requires a substantial argument to establish it. Further, if the mechanism that dictates hypothesis plausibilities does admit zero, almost surely, values for some hypotheses, perhaps the "very low probability" of the existence of God actually could be zero, almost surely. If this is correct, Richard Dawkins could potentially describe himself as a 6.999... ("six-point-nine-repeating") on his Spectrum. As noted, technically, 6.999... equals 7, but since he defined a seven as "Strong atheist. 'I know there is no God, with the same conviction as Jung knows there is one,'" perhaps this justifies the use of the repeating-nines, a nonstandard form of that number, if only as a rhetorical device.

Dot, Dot, Dot

13

Bayes Without Priors

The end of the previous chapter raises such a fascinating question about how we assign plausibilities to hypotheses that it needs further development on its own. Here, I wish to discuss the matter of how investigating the plausibilities of certain kinds of hypotheses strikes to the heart of some aspects of Bayesian reasoning, a useful method by which we can assess how likely our hypotheses are to be true.

. . .

I have been informed by a mathematician friend of mine that the trying to make statements about the plausibility of the God hypothesis may pick a nit with Bayesian reasoning in a way that may be significant. He also pointed out that it's not original to either of us,[20] but that I might be highlighting its importance and thus its use in the discussion about God. I merely want to mention it here without going thoroughly into the development of the idea, its history, or even into the details of Bayesian reasoning.

A brief aside to get a sense of Bayesian reasoning is needed, though. The essence is that using a mathematical result known as *Bayes's Theorem*, which is a very basic result within probability theory, we can get a decent grasp on how evidence impacts our confi-

---

[20]   He notes several sources that influenced his thinking, including Elliott Sober and Ian Hacking. A quick search for papers on "Bayes without priors" illustrates that the idea is out there.

dence in a hypothesis. A bit more formally, we can make some estimates about how likely it is that we see what we see, in light of the hypothesis in question, and then this relatively basic mathematical theorem allows us to update our assessment. Our less-informed *prior* confidence in the validity of the hypothesis is improved into a more-informed *posterior* confidence in it. These terms need some clarification.

Before considering the evidence, in a Bayesian analysis we could estimate (or "guesstimate") how likely it seems that our hypothesis is accurate. We call this estimate the "prior probability," or "prior" for short, because it's what we think prior to looking at the evidence. Then, by using Bayes's Theorem, we attempt to evaluate the role of evidence to obtain a "posterior probability," or "posterior" for short, that we accept as being more informed and thus likely to be nearer to the actual plausibility of our hypothesis. The mechanism of applying Bayes's Theorem requires us to estimate some probabilities that evaluate the evidence in light of our hypothesis, a problem that can be quite difficult in its own right and a source of interesting debate.[21]

To quickly make a note, the interpretation of probability that arises from Bayesian reasoning is classified as being "subjective probability." The reason comes down to the subjective nature of assigning the prior. A raging debate in its own right centers on the question of whether or not "objective priors" exist, but even if they do, there are sound arguments that indicate that

---

[21] For more information, see *Evidence and Evolution* by Elliott Sober, for instance, listed in the recommended reading at the end of this book.

the other probabilities used to do the machinery of Bayes's Theorem (known as "consequents") are also necessarily determined subjectively.

As it turns out, Bayesian reasoning has an important caveat to it: as a rule, one cannot assign priors that indicate certainty (those being zero and one). The ultimate reason is that when a certain plausibility, zero or one, is input as the prior, the posterior always comes out the same value, zero or one, respectively, no matter what the evidence says. In other words, Bayes's Theorem tells us what certainty means: no claim to evidence could possibly change our estimate of plausibility.

Now, technically, on "almost sure" priors, evidence that points "almost surely" the other way could plausibly be sufficient, using the rules of calculus, to obtain a different posterior probability. I might argue that regarding something like the existence of Klingons, we could assign an almost-surely-zero prior and then, if we were to meet an actual Klingon, use that as almost-surely-certain evidence that they exist and overcome this problem. I don't think my personal view here is remotely considered mainstream, however, and the usual Bayesian rule rejects assigning almost certain priors as well. This may be another interesting philosophical point to ponder regarding the use of Bayesian reasoning, but it is outside of my scope to go into it.

There's another matter to consider here. A problem arises when we examine certain kinds of hypotheses: those that do not admit to testing by in-principle identical, repeatable experiments. A hypothesis like the existence of God constitutes one such example, and so using Bayesian reasoning to consider the question is a

145

very difficult matter to undertake, despite both noble[22] and ignoble[23] efforts.

Particularly, as the previous chapter indicates, we have an issue with assigning a prior plausibility to the "God" hypothesis. In a sense, only the "almost sure" cases seem to have any defensible philosophical purchase. Indeed, we do not have sufficient reason—based upon a complete paucity of evidence—to assign any positive prior to the plausibility of the existence of God, and yet the axioms of Bayesian reasoning pre-clude assigning anything but a positive prior plausibility on this hypothesis. Even if a case could be made for almost certain existence of God, Bayesian reasoning precludes assigning it as a prior. What can we do? Don't assign one—leave it undefined.

Perhaps surprisingly, this decision isn't fatal. In-deed, it is informative to do a Bayes-informed analysis in this and similar cases without ever assigning a prior plausibility. It can work because we know that what-ever the prior might be, the role of evidence will usually push the posterior one way or the other. In some situations, the evidence will uniformly push our estimate of the posterior in one direction only.

There's even a ready example. Given that super-naturalism has lost to natural explanations in *literally every case* that has been examined, the hypothesis of God's existence, which depends upon supernatural-

---

22   E.g. Carrier, Richard (2012), *Proving History: Bayes's Theorem and the Quest for a Historical Jesus*, Amherst, NY: Prometheus.

23   E.g. Unwin, Stephen D. (2004), *The Probability of God: A Simple Calculation That Proves the Ultimate Truth*, New York: Three Rivers Press.

ism, yet again is one such hypothesis. This apparently huge claim is captured formally by Jeffrey Jay Lowder's Argument From the History of Science[24] and essentially restates historian Richard Carrier's increasingly famous Bayesian argument that naturalism has always been the winning horse to bet on so far as explanations for phenomena go.

Thus, while perhaps we cannot assign a zero, almost surely, prior plausibility with regard to the existence of God, we can still make a clear statement about what direction the evidence is pushing the posterior. The posterior plausibility of the God hypothesis has been *uniformly decreased* as we've collected evidence that should bear upon that question. In Carrier's metaphor, the God hypotheses, in any form specific enough to consider, has lost millions of races and simply should not be bet upon to win any in the future.[25]

Generally, then, it is not strictly necessary to assign a prior plausibility to a hypothesis in order to glean a solid Bayesian result, since evidence that pushes the posterior in one direction only can tell us everything that we need to know to draw our conclusion. In the case of the God hypothesis, given the

---

[24]   Lowder, Jeffery Jay, "The Evidential Argument from the History of Science (AHS), *The Secular Outpost*, http://www.patheos.com/blogs/ secularoutpost/2012/06/16/the-evidential-argument-from-the-history-of-science-ahs/ (retrieved August 15, 2013).

[25]   Carrier, Richard (2006), "Naturalism is True, Theism is Not: Carrier's Opening Statement", Carrier-Wanchick Debate, *The Secular Web*, http://www.infidels.org/library/modern/richard_carrier/carrier-wanchick/carrier1.html (retrieved August 15, 2013).

amount of evidence we have now—considering the Problem of Evil, the uniform discovery of natural causes, the utter lack of explanatory power of the God hypothesis, and the distributions of contradictory world religions—just to touch the tip of the iceberg—it is hardly controversial to assign an incredibly low *posterior* plausibility to the God hypothesis.

But there is controversy on this point, and there is a lot of it. Religious believers do not assess the evidence in the same way as those without belief in some God, and thus they see the matter the other way around. Christians, for example, read the evidence in a way that uniformly *increases* the posterior plausibility that God exists and that Christ is God. Importantly, this same kind of thing is true for other religious believers with their own beliefs as well (details varying accordingly).

The global religious variety, while undercutting credence in specific interpretations, offers a compelling suggestion as to the main reason that believers interpret the evidence in their favor: cognitive biases. I would suggest that faith itself is a cognitive bias, but it is one built upon others. Notably, confirmation bias allows religious believers to interpret evidence according to their beliefs while dismissing that which goes against them. Notice that Christians, Muslims, Hindus, and others all believe wildly contradictory claims about the same world, each citing their own faith-based interpretations of the data to support them.

To lay it more bare, look at how the varying faiths interpret the same evidence. Fundamentalist Christians have interpreted earthquakes as punishment from God for giving homosexuals a chance at equal treatment before the law. Fundamentalist Muslims have interpreted earthquakes as warnings from Allah for women dressing immodestly. Some more liberal believers have interpreted these events as having been caused or allowed to happen so as to teach people personal lessons of strength or compassion. Neither can these claims can be verified directly, nor do any of them have utilizable explanatory power. They also follow, and do not lead, belief. Notice, for instance, that the fundamentalists' claims could easily be tested (while the liberals' are exercises in solipsism). Unsurprisingly, however rigorously the tests were done, the fundamentalists' beliefs are unlikely to be shaken. This is how confirmation bias works.

In fairness, we should ask if informed skeptics are also guilty of confirmation bias. Of course, we're all susceptible to it, but in the meaningful sense in this context, I argue not. The reasons are found in the reliability of predictions made on testable hypotheses. The predictions made by science are staggeringly accurate, and this is undeniable. Further, informed skeptics like scientists do not generally have an attachment to a particular outcome and actively work to overcome confirmation bias by a variety of effective means. However shocking it might be to find it out, for example, if rigorous testing discovered that homosexuals and scantily clad women really did cause earthquakes, then so be it. Faith enjoys far less elbow room in this regard.

Within Christianity, for example, one such testable hypothesis was allegedly offered by Jesus when he advised us that what we pray for in faith we will receive. To date, no prayer for a miraculous regrowth of an amputated limb, or any other such thing, has succeeded. Surely such prayers have been prayed! Also people around the world, including innocent children and their desperate parents, wail in prayers to Jesus for food, and yet they starve. Any one of us can try it now, praying for anything tangible and unlikely, and the chance that it will occur will match exactly the chance that it would have occurred anyway by sheer coincidence.

This isn't to pick on Christianity. Islam and every other religion fare identically—Pagan spells don't work either. On the other hand, without any appeal to God at all, whether investigated by a believer or not, a prediction that a rocket fired under specific conditions will safely transport a human being to the moon and back is *reliably* successful. Informed skepticism doubts until it can't, and belief believes even after it shouldn't.

Referring back to the earthquake example above, geologists insist that tremors are caused by consequences of plate tectonics. Further, they gladly attest that literally anyone can observe the relevant data if they so desire, and if the evidence were to point to a different mechanism than proposed, say hydraulic fracking or even gatherings of flamboyant gays, the geologists would change their minds to follow that evidence. This suggests that the believers are the ones misled by cognitive biases that cause them to misinterpret the evidence and arrive at mistaken posterior plausibilities for the objects of their beliefs.

To come back to theme, then: How low a chance can we claim for the posterior for the existence of God? I'd suggest, at this point on this discussion, that we could say that the plausibility of the God hypothesis is at least *negligibly low*, if playing within Bayesian boundaries, unable to say "almost sure." In other words, whatever the plausibility of the hypothesis actually is, if we absolutely can't claim zero, it is still by far small enough to ignore it entirely. This doesn't rule out that God exists, but it backs my thinking that the level of evidence that I would require at this point would be the same as the evidence I'd require to accept that the Force or Klingons exist.

Still, I stand by my case that we should seriously consider assigning an almost-surely zero plausibility to God's existence on three main points. First, as it is not categorical denial, it may be philosophically defensible. Second, there are no credible arguments that suggest any positive plausibility to God's existence that would refute it. And third, when we look at the evidence, it has uniformly been pushed in one direction: down toward zero, almost surely, the lowest philosophically defensible value admissible on the question. In light of these points, concluding that the plausibility is zero, almost surely, is not much of a stretch, if it stretches at all.

The primary obstacle is simply that Bayesian reasoning does not admit almost surely zero assignments of plausibility. While Bayesian reasoning may be right as it is, it may also have some issues with it at its edges. Immediately troubling, for instance, is the requirement that every potential hypothesis must be granted and retain some plausibility, no matter how ridiculous! These loose seams conceivably could be dealt with in a number of ways, but each, as usual, is a choice on our part and carries consequences. Also, of course, since Bayesian reasoning has stood up quite well in practice, it is unlikely to be wise to throw it away entirely, although some clarification may be needed to handle these issues.

One possibility is to attempt to frame up a theoretical basis for how "almost sure" probabilities can be handled in a Bayesian analysis. Another is to formally define a term like *paradigm* to refer to the (necessarily finite) collection of hypotheses that we give any consideration to at all beyond a default status of "almost surely not." In other words, hearkening back to the analogy of the infinitely large bag, this use of the term "paradigm" would roughly define where we fuzz out the edges of an infinite sample space of potential hypotheses. Yet again, let me point out how human this reveals our efforts to make sense of the world to be, including philosophy and even mathematics, and especially theology.

A significant challenge to this "paradigm" approach is that the paradigms will necessarily shift over time, literally changing which hypotheses are valid to consider and which aren't. Was quantum mechanics part of the paradigm, for instance, in Isaac Newton's day? This notion would need some serious philosophical architecture before gaining any real traction.

My argument that the existence of God has probability zero, almost surely, would be seen from this perspective as arguing that the God hypothesis has been removed from the paradigm now, effectively by science and secularism triumphing over superstition and even tradition.

• • •
Infinity and Ontological Arguments
• • •

Ontology is the branch of philosophy that deals with existence—a matter of central importance, in a way, if we are to discuss infinity and other abstract objects. Theologians and philosophers have long sought ontological arguments that prove the philosophical necessity of various ideas, not least the idea(s) called "God." Many of these arguments are quite famous, and many of them incorporate infinity or ideas that are related to it. It is my intention in this section, partly using the thrust that the most that we are able to say is that infinity is an abstract notion, to reveal ontologically argued Gods as abstractions as well. This would indicate that ontological arguments for "God" are almost never worth the paper they're printed upon, much less the time it takes to concoct them.

Dot, Dot, Dot

14

Richard Carrier's *Ex Nihilo* and 63%

This chapter represents a slight diversion from criticizing the use of the infinite in arguing for God. Instead, here, I want to address an argument from the historian and prolific author Richard Carrier that uses the concept of the infinite to argue *against* God. I hope it is clear that my intention is to illustrate the potential for folly involved in making appeals to the infinite in any kind of ontological argument, and particularly, I want to let this discussion open onto a richer field of attacking ontological-style arguments *for* God. To be charitable, I try to save as much from Carrier's approach as I think may be able to be claimed.

. . .

On the blog he keeps on the *Freethoughtblogs* network, historian Richard Carrier attempts to tackle the classic *ex nihilo* argument often presented by religious philosophers. Its usual, classical expression is "*ex nihilo nihil fit*," or "out of nothing, nothing comes." The essential argument theologians like to attempt via *ex nihilo* is that since it is not logically possible for nothing to give rise to something, and because we see something, there must be some kind of primordial or eternal something that gave rise to the entire universe. Via a variety of *ad hoc* definitions and properties ascribed to this primeval something, the theologian contends that this "something" must indeed be "God."

It is important to note that the "God" in question here is actually the "God" named in Deism, or less. Deism asserts only that a deity was required to cause the universe. Particularly, we cannot conclude from Deism, hence such an apologetic argument, that said deity has any discernible dealings with the universe since causing it to exist. It's also worth pausing to remember that this is the same deity argued for by the Kalām Cosmological Argument that Christian and Muslim apologists both imagine makes a case for their beliefs.

Apologists, despite their attempts, seem to give no good answers to why an agent "God" is required instead of simply admitting that the universe itself could be the primeval "something." In other words, the concept of *nihilo* simply might not be realistically coherent. Equally important to note, modern cosmologists, Lawrence Krauss the most famous, report that what we mean by "nothing," in the sense of the universe, is not the same as the absolute nothing proposed by philosophers.[26] These ideas together may render the *ex nihilo* argument something of a non-starter.

Turning to Richard Carrier, he applies some snark by naming his *ex nihilo* argument "*Ex Nihilo Onus Merdae Fit,*"[27] which I am translating roughly as "out of nothing comes a load of shit." I would expect this to be

---

[26]   Cf. Krauss, Lawrence (2013), *A Universe From Nothing: Why There is Something Rather than Nothing*, New York: Atria.

[27]   Carrier, Richard (2012), "Ex Nihilo Onus Merdae Fit," Richard Carrier Blogs, http://freethoughtblogs.com/carrier/archives/468 (retrieved August 7, 2013).

a double entendre expressing that the *ex nihilo* argument itself is a "load of shit" and that he wants to make the case that lots and lots of things come out of hypothetical *nihilo*. Carrier's argument proceeds upon the "assumptions of theism," that *nihilo* essentially means only that which is logically necessary exists. It is of importance to note that Carrier does not assume *nihilo* of this or any kind to have been a true situation in the universe. He is analyzing the hypothesis in a conditional sense, which is to say that he starts with a great big, often-overlooked *if* that we would do well to recognize to avoid creating a straw man of his view.

In the interest of full disclosure, Carrier asked me to evaluate his use of the notion of infinity in this argument. I did so and do not agree with his application. I feel there are fundamental errors in his argument, which he has attempted to defend with me at length. I'm not writing this specifically to refute Carrier or his argument, though, but rather to point out three things interesting to my purposes with this book. First, there are certain abuses of the notion of infinity that I would like to point out. Second, I think all arguments of this kind confuse the abstract for the real—a problematic confusion of the map and the terrain that defines Platonism. Third, while I think such *a priori* ontological arguments are effectively pointless, if we bend some rules in the name of armchairing our philosophy, I don't think Carrier's conclusion is completely lost; it just reaches too far.

Carrier's argument proceeds from a central premise that is worth naming for reference, as he does. It is stated as "P1: In the beginning there was absolutely nothing." I feel I absolutely must point out the use of the dubious phrase "in the beginning," but it isn't worth harping on. Immediately, he extends P1 to a

157

second premise explicitly elaborating upon his specific meaning: "P2: If there was absolutely nothing, then (apart from logical necessity) there existed absolutely nothing to prevent anything from happening or to make any one thing happening any more likely than any other thing."

Already we are running into some dodgy ideas. Particularly, I feel that Carrier tends toward the error that logic can have a deterministic effect on the universe (instead of being a tool via which we create and understand abstract models of the reality of which we are a part). This is a problem we see in all ontological arguments for the existence of God as well, so Carrier's use may follow the theologian's nose here. Importantly, of course, this position is the Platonic one. There's an inherent danger here in that thinking logical necessity can "cause" things to happen in reality because it confuses the map for the terrain it attempts to describe.

Also, I find the phrase "to make any one thing happening any more likely than any other thing" worrisome. The reason is that it explicitly lays out an assumption of a uniform probability distribution on the sample space of potential "things happening." If the probability distribution is assumed to be uniform, as we have seen, then we are required to conclude (by logical necessity) that the sample space of potential things that can happen is *finite* if discrete or in some way bounded if continuous. Carrier's is neither. As discussed at length previously, infinite-measure sample spaces cannot be equipped with a uniform probability distribution because such a thing is meaningless.

Of course, Carrier makes the obvious deduction from these two propositions: [if] there was absolutely nothing (apart from logical necessity) "in the beginning," then there is nothing to prevent anything from happening or to make any one thing happening more likely than any other thing. Please note that I have inserted the word *if* in brackets because I think it is important for us to remind ourselves of the conditional nature of the proposition P1 we're assuming for the argument. It is, in fact, worth indicating that in many such ontological-style arguments the conditional upon which they all hinge is often lost.

Carrier's argument gets harder to work with almost immediately. His next proposition reads:

> Of all the logically possible things that can happen when nothing exists to prevent them from happening, continuing to be nothing is one thing, one universe popping into existence is another thing, two universes popping into existence is yet another thing, and so on all the way to *infinitely many* universes popping into existence, *and likewise for every cardinality of infinity*, and every configuration of universes. [emphasis mine]

I have some pretty serious concerns about this statement. Carrier introduces it as a proposition, though, meaning something he is assuming for the sake of the argument he is making. On his definition of *nihilo*, this seems plausible, but it sweeps a great deal of important detail under the rug, only some of which Carrier accounts for.

First, and perhaps foremost, this is a very odd way to categorize the things that could possibly happen. One universe could pop into existence—in how many different ways? What constitutes a universe? Are all universes equally likely kinds of universes? One universe popping into existence doesn't necessarily

159

represent one possible outcome, then, a problem that is compounded exponentially when we get to more than one universe. Carrier accounts for this point with "and every configuration of universes," and he correctly notes that it seems to work in his favor because there are many, many ways that *more* universes could "pop into existence" (also odd but no more odd than an uncaused agent deity causing them to exist) and yet only one way in which nothing would continue to be nothing.

Now more fatally, we see that there is also nothing to prevent "infinitely many universes popping into existence, and likewise for every cardinality of infinity." Carrier is asserting that every possibility is equally likely since there is nothing to prevent any potential outcome from occurring. We already possess logical impossibility that infinitely many discrete outcomes can all have equal likelihood, so something is fundamentally broken at this stage in the argument. The way Carrier seeks to get around this problem is by claiming that infinitesimal probabilities save the day, but as noted previously, not only are they a fringe topic in analysis, they lack the necessary coherence to make sense out of. Here, then, I'm pointing out an abuse of the notion of infinity.

Carrier's argument proceeds by arguing explicitly that each of these potential outcomes should, indeed, have equal probability:

> If each outcome (0 universes, 1 universe, 2 universes, etc. all the way to aleph-0 universes, aleph-1 universes, etc. [*note that there is more than one infinity in this sequence*]) is no more likely than the next, then the probability of any finite number of universes (including zero universes) *or less* having popped into existence is infinitely close to zero, and the probability of some infinite

160

number of universes having popped into existence is
infinitely close to one hundred percent. [his emphasis]

For clarity with his terms, "aleph_0" is the name of
the cardinality of the smallest infinite set, "aleph_1"
the next smallest infinite cardinality, etc. These terms
assume the acceptance of the continuum hypothesis,
which amounts to accepting an axiom that lets us
think of the sizes of infinity discretely like this. If we
reject the continuum hypothesis instead, the sequence
of infinite cardinals he provides doesn't really have any
meaning because it would mean we can't make a
sequence of that kind because there are too many sizes
of infinity!

In either case, we hardly need to point out that we
may have left reality entirely behind to believe that
"infinitely many universes almost surely *must* exist"
merely on the assumption of "in the beginning there
was absolutely nothing." Richard Dawkins's famous
criticism of ontological arguments as being word
games that do not look at a single datum from the real
world[28] feels quite fitting here, in fact. But, in fairness,
let us remind ourselves of the conditional nature of
this entire enterprise and the fact that Carrier does not
claim to believe that *nihilo* was ever reality.

As we saw when exploring the idea of cheating and
forcing a uniform distribution on an unbounded
infinite set, we could conclude that a finite number is
never going to occur, so Carrier's conclusion that we
would have an infinite number of universes in existence is, *if we assume this violation of coherence,*

---

[28]   Dawkins, Richard (2006), *The God Delusion*, New York:
Bantam, pp. 105-7.

essentially correct. We immediately face the question of "which infinity?" though, because there are infinitely many possibilities to choose from. This question poses a problem.

Particularly, recall that as with numbers, every infinity is smaller than most. As we saw with the numbers, this property is, in essence, the reason that a uniform distribution illegally forced upon on the natural numbers would never return a numerical value. Well, because every infinite cardinal is also necessarily smaller than most, the question of "which infinity?" here is worse than impossible to answer. Not only could we not tell which one it is, we could know with certainty that every possible choice is wrong.

Now, this is weird and worth lingering over for a bit. What happened with the numbers, if we look closely, is that we punted the possible selection beyond the strong limit cardinal called "countable infinity." Given any number, we can be sure we'd never pick a value less than that because only finitely many are less while infinitely many are more. Analogously, under such a forced uniform distribution of the kind Carrier suggests that applies also to all infinite cardinals, we can be sure that we'd never pick an infinite cardinal smaller than any specified because there are only finitely many below it (on Carrier's construction) and infinitely many larger. Thus, we should have to punt again similarly.

To where, though, could we punt? We might conclude that every finite value *and* every infinite value is incorrect. Thus, perhaps we would need a concept that goes beyond the notion of "infinite" in the same way that "infinite" goes beyond the notion of finite, that is beyond a strong limit cardinal profoundly larger than *every* "infinite" cardinal. It is unclear if doing so would create an infinite ascension of needing to do so, under Carrier's construction. In fact, it is not at all clear what any of this means or that it can have meaning at all.

I want to be maximally charitable to Carrier's argument, though, and I see no strong reason to dismiss his conclusion that *if* universes were popping at random into existence without any rule to tell us about how or why they do so, then we would have infinitely many of them—only that the various cardinalities of infinity make a real mess of the question. This is his construction, and although I feel it is a bit odd and fanciful, as a mental exercise it isn't a completely bankrupt exploration. I just don't think it has anything to do with physical reality, and I don't think Carrier does either.

To continue, then, Carrier introduces one last proposition to his argument:

> If there are infinitely many universes, and our universe has a nonzero probability of existing (as by existing it proves it does, via *cogito ergo sum*), then the probability that our universe would exist is infinitely close to one hundred percent (because any nonzero probability approaches one hundred percent as the number of selections approaches infinity, via the infinite monkey theorem, similar to the law of large numbers).

From this proposition, Carrier concludes that upon his P1 (absolutely nothing except logical necessity), our universe would exist with probability one, almost surely, which is to say that *nihilo* together with logic alone *requires* our universe to exist, barring a completely implausible set of possibilities.

Recall that the infinite monkey theorem (which is not really similar to the law of large numbers, incidentally) states that given infinitely many trials, any

163

possible occurrence with nonzero probability will occur with almost certainty. For example, if I had an infinite string of random digits, zero through nine, the infinite monkey theorem guarantees, almost surely, that we will find somewhere in that string every American's social security number, listed back-to-back in alphabetical order by their names. The infinite monkey theorem is the relevant point I want to discuss in this proposition because I don't think Carrier's construction has the power to use it the way he wants to.

Let's start with the *cogito ergo sum* point. What we have is almost sure information that our universe exists—unless perhaps we get weird about the definition of "exists." From that we can conclude that our universe doesn't have a likelihood of existence that is exactly zero (logical impossibility). What we don't have is any way to assess how unlikely our universe is in a situation like Carrier's imaginary exploration, in which infinitely many universes pop into existence out of nothing. For all we know, our universe could be the only one that could support us out of the infinitely many Carrier asserts must have come into existence—all he needs is possibility. It could also be that infinitely many universes similar to ours could exist but that the cardinality of total universes is a vastly larger infinity. Not only do we not know, we have no way of knowing from the propositions in his construction. In short, we don't know enough to be able to apply the infinite monkey theorem here.

The infinite monkey theorem works because it considers infinitely many trials against an event with a classically nonzero probability of occurrence. By "classically nonzero probability," I mean events that have odds of the form one-in-n, for some finite *number* n, in other words, a probability that is strictly not zero.

164

With strings of numbers, even if a particular social security number is quite unlikely—a one in one billion occurrence—it is not probability-zero. Thus, the infinite monkey theorem can give an almost sure guarantee that it occurs somewhere in the infinite sequence of decimal digits because the chance that it would never occur gets vanishingly small as the length of the string grows ever longer.

By extension into questions of events that are infinitely unlikely, as seem to be needed for Carrier's argument, it *may* be reasonable to conclude that the infinite monkey theorem sometimes applies. I actually do not know this or even know if it is known or knowable—there are some very subtle counterexamples of apparently "true" ideas when dealing with the analysis of infinite sets. For instance, it seems reasonable to conclude that if we use a sufficiently large infinite cardinality of trials, probability zero events might be guaranteed. Let me reiterate: *might be* the case. This whole line of thought stinks of nonsense, though, because it doesn't seem to make sense to talk about an uncountably infinite number of repeated trials, which is certainly the quantity needed to rescue any event with probability zero, almost surely.

This unlikely bigger-infinity-against-smaller-infinity possibility doesn't help us much, even if we grant that it has meaning. We do not have any way to conclude that the number of universes that "popped into existence" in Carrier's construction is sufficiently large to counteract the unlikeliness of our universe under his assumptions. I would argue, perhaps, that *cogito ergo sum* could let us contend that the cardinality of infinity representing the number of universes that "popped into existence" (again, pretending that this makes sense, although it doesn't) should be the

165

same cardinality that represents the length of the odds against our universe doing so. Otherwise, a universe like ours would almost certainly *not* exist, contradicting *cogito ergo sum.*

If that's the case, the infinite monkey theorem does not apply, and we cannot conclude certainty as Carrier wishes. In other words, even if we grant all of Carrier's premises and questionable uses of infinity up to this point, he cannot make an argument that the infinite monkey theorem applies, which he needs to conclude (almost) certainty that our universe exists on *ex nihilo.*

All may not be not lost, though. Why? Because another mathematical principle may apply—again, supposing we grant all of the abuses of infinity up to the point of the infinite monkey theorem's application. We should note that the fact that this possibility even exists precludes Carrier's ability to use *cogito ergo sum* to argue that our universe must have a sufficiently large likelihood for the infinite monkey theorem to apply.

It is fairly well-known that if we have a particular random event with odds of a stated length, say one in one thousand, and we apply a trial for that event the same number of times as the length of the odds, here one thousand times, the likelihood that we would see that event occur at least once tends toward a specific number that is close to 63% as the number of trials gets larger and the unlikeliness of the event gets proportionally smaller. (Precisely, the number is $1-(1/e)$, where e is the famous natural exponential base, roughly 2.71828 in value.) While I do not think that Carrier's argument as written can be used to conclude this, I'll suggest that it could possibly be rewritten more cautiously to draw this conclusion if he desired to do so, granting some borderline abuses and possibly a use of a monolithic concept of infinity, at the least. To be fair, note that apologists for God often ask us to grant far greater abuses in their arguments.

So, if we allow all of Carrier's premises here and permit him to use his arguments about infinitesimals to avoid the impossibility of applying a uniform distribution in the manner he intends, I do not see it as utterly unreasonable to conclude that given *ex nihilo* with logical necessity, a universe like ours could have a 63% chance of random occurrence. This isn't the certainty with which Carrier wants so he can drive a nail into the *ex nihilo* argument, but it's far, far better than the terrible "out of nothing comes nothing; therefore, God" given by theologians.

Yet again, and most importantly, because of the nature of ontological arguments of this kind, it is wise to remind ourselves that Carrier does not explicitly endorse the *ex nihilo* hypothesis he calls P1. Specifically, we should pay attention to the fact that his antitheistic argument, just like theistic ones of similar construction, feel overwhelmingly like someone played a word game so as to pull an abstract rabbit out of a nonexistent hat. Carrier appears to have the integrity to know this about it. Still, here we have yet another signpost to be very cautious about confusing the map for the terrain.

Dot, Dot, Dot

15

About Gödel's Ontological Argument

To be up front about it, this chapter has the least to do with infinity of all the ones included in this collection. Because of the instrumental work done by Kurt Gödel when it comes to understanding what we can know about abstract ideas, though, a note about his onto-logical argument for the existence of God is worth inclusion—if only to quell objections that I haven't addressed it. I think it gives some insight to the overall uselessness of ontological arguments, even when they don't invoke infinity or appeal to specific theology. Indeed, I hope this also makes the point that being an absolutely brilliant logician, as Gödel unquestionably was, does not exempt someone from the possibility of conflating logic and reality—a point I consider of paramount importance in the discussion concerning the God hypothesis.

· · ·

Many apologists and theologians, flexing philosophical, like to mention what, at bottom, is Kurt Gödel's ontological argument for the existence of "God." Gödel's argument is pretty much impenetrable gobble-degook, in that it's written in formal logic. To very loosely paraphrase it, and to capture the spirit of the typical religious debater using it, it essentially suggests that if God is logically possible in all possible worlds, then God necessarily exists. It draws a comparison between "God," defined as some kind of necessary, self-existent, and, of course, immaterial being, to be contrasted with "contingent" beings like ourselves, in that our existence requires matter and energy in our universe and this God does not. Through some artful use of axioms and then ironclad logic upon them, people following these arguments seem to produce a God out of nothing. The trick is that the axioms themselves defined the God they're defending.

Gödel's proof is a bit involved (Wikipedia contains a full summary, for the curious), so for brevity, I will not outline it here. Indeed, the proof itself is air-tight, revealing that the problems at the heart of it are somewhere else. We'll examine the axioms that under-lie it, hopefully clarifying how axioms can lead to abstract ideas that feel very real. I will also point out that the proof follows modal logic, which is rather thoroughly worthless for making serious existence claims about reality—in exactly the manner that confuses the map for the terrain.

In order to explore it, instead of refuting Gödel's ontological proof of the existence of God, I will concede it. The relevant ball to keep our eye upon is what it gets us. Hint: it is not what apologists want it to prove. To briefly summarize what Gödel is trying to prove, I will list the underlying assumptions that he makes, those explicitly referred to as axioms. He assumes six axioms along with three definitions. The axioms[29] are

1. Any property entailed by a positive property is positive.

---

29   Source: *Wikipedia* entry for Gödel's ontological argument.

2. If a property is positive, then its negation is not positive.
3. The property of being God-like is positive.
4. If a property is positive, then it is necessarily positive.
5. Necessary existence is a positive property.
6. For any property P, if P is positive, then being necessarily P is positive.

Gödel's definitions are important to consider, particularly in light of his third axiom, which employs the specific terminology "God-like." Those definitions are

1. X is *God-like* if and only if X has as essential properties those and only those properties which are positive.
2. A is an *essence* of X if and only if for every property B, X has B if and only if A entails B.
3. X *necessarily exists* if and only if every essence of X is necessarily exemplified.

To briefly touch on the axioms here, I'd like to draw attention to the fifth axiom, though qualms can be raised with all of them. Because of the definition of being "God-like," it is quite easy to read it as if God possesses the property of necessary existence simply by brute force. This should feel a bit dodgy, but even if granted as legitimate, it reveals the shackles put on God by defining it this way.

Now, and this is a primary criticism, since Gödel arrives at this notion of this "God" by examining axioms, the (abstract) concept of God that he establishes is also *subject to* those axioms. That means two things. First, if those axioms are bad or don't match

171

reality, then there's a problem with claiming that the "God" subject to them has anything to do with reality as well. It also means that the "God" it defines is merely an abstraction, and so people whose defenses of a God rely upon this abstraction are likely to be misleading themselves. Certainly also, this definition of "God" is not the personal God that most believers claim is real. For those of us who don't believe in God, importantly, arguments of this kind provide no compelling reasons to change our minds.

Furthermore, because this "God" is defined via these axioms, and not supported by credible evidence, we have a fairly good reason to expect that whatever "God" Gödel is proving is just some kind of an abstraction, not an existent being. If his proof proves that "God" exists, it only proves that *this* weird concept of "God" exists, one that is by definition a moral aesthetic positive captured in the definition of being "God-like." Wouldn't it be better just to say that Gödel proved that a certain kind of moral aesthetic, itself an abstraction, necessarily "exists," in the abstract way? The term "God," here, then is a bad metaphor because it is very unlikely to be read the way it was written. As is often the case, then, bad metaphors help maintain the God delusion.

What does this tell us? In essence, it shows that any attempt to lay out axioms to prove God exists subjects God to a definition created by those axioms. Furthermore, such a "God" is an axiomatic, thus abstract, construction that is a bad metaphor since people will confuse it with their favorite deity. So, if we want to follow Gödel and define God as an arbitrary and abstract moral-aesthetic positive that if it exists in one possible world then it must exist in all possible worlds, then maybe his ontological proof proves that

James A. Lindsay

"God" exists; the God worshiped in world religions lying on the other side of even more assumptions and assertions.

Who cares, though? And why should anyone care? Who prays to *that* "God" or goes to church to sing *"his"* praises? What has *this* "God" to do with Christianity or Islam or Hinduism or Paganism? Christians, for instance, will argue that this *is* their God, but to do so requires essentially all of their work to still lie ahead of them!

The problem left by such an *a priori* argument is that impossible chasms of *non sequitur* (literally "it does not follow") have to be leaped to get from that particular definition to the ones that are actually used by people, notably the Gods of faiths like Christianity, Islam, Judaism, Hinduism, etc. For Christians to accept Gödel's "God" as theirs, for instance, requires them to accept that this God created the universe we are in necessarily as a moral positive. Further, they have to believe that this God created it in a way in which sin could exist, requiring him to send himself as his son to Earth to be tortured and executed to atone for that sin. This is but one among a number of challenging propositions. Note also that Gödel's construction implies that if his modal "God" is the God of Christianity, then all of the Christian story is a necessary positive. It is my opinion that accepting that statement requires quite a stretch of the meaning of the words "moral aesthetic," or for a more apologetic turn of phrase, "moral perfection."

If proofs like Gödel's above don't commit it on their own, then, the question begging begins in obscene amounts the very moment we try to extend these very weird ontological definitions of "God" to other meanings of that word. This ontological "God" is not

173

necessarily connected to a cosmological or teleological "God," nor is it obviously connected to the objects of belief of Christians and other religious believers. It is instead a Platonic God, a philosopher's God. Establishing a connection to their beliefs is completely necessary to claiming validity for any theistic religion that can even be conceived of, and Gödel's proof doesn't provide it.

16

Anselm's Ontological Whiff

This final chapter is actually an updated excerpt from the sixth chapter of my first book *God Doesn't; We Do: Only Humans Can Solve Human Challenges*. In that chapter I endeavored to tackle several of the more famous apologetic arguments for God's existence, and a specific one that held the door open to modern mathematical analysis is Anselm's Ontological Argument. Anselm of Canterbury was an 11th and 12th century theologian—in fact the Archbishop of Canterbury for a time—who has since been canonized. His argument for the existence of God, a stupendous game of wordplay, centered upon a definition of God as "that than which nothing higher can be conceived." As I hope you realize by now, that idea itself is incoherent under careful analysis.

. . .

Of all of the arguments for God's existence, the ontological argument sometimes is argued to have the highest philosophical value. To say that it has a decent amount of philosophical value, though, does not get it anywhere with proving the existence of God, particularly since, even if it were correct, it floats in the murky *non sequitur* sea of unjustified leaps from "something we call 'God' exists" to "my God exists." This argument, like all of the other philosophical arguments for the existence of God, merely points to the philosopher's God, not to any particular manifesta-

175

tion of it as revealed in the various scriptures, leaving the apologist to bridge the gap to the object of their belief after defending the ontological claim. Interestingly, the claim that it has "highest" philosophical value is a fairly weak one, as the ontological argument is essentially a play on words.

Like the dead horse which is Pascal's Wager, the ontological argument has been thoroughly thrashed, even including humorous reformulations that produce the reverse results. We have St. Anselm in the eleventh century to thank for this nifty piece of imprecise thinking, which former preacher, now infidel, John Loftus generously claims gives him the sense of having just watched a "really good magician" in action. Here is what the ontological argument says, according to St. Anselm, numbered as presented by Loftus in *Why I Became an Atheist*[30]:

1. On the assumption that "that than which nothing greater can be conceived" is only in a mind, something greater can be conceived because
2. something greater can be thought to exist in reality as well.
3. The results of this assumption are therefore contradictory and must be rejected: either there is no such thing even in the intellect or it exists also in reality;
4. but it does exist in the mind of the fool (making an appeal to Psalms 14:1, where the original Hebrew for fool here refers to someone that is

[30]   Loftus, John W (2008), *Why I Became an Atheist: A Former Preacher Rejects Christianity*, Amherst: Prometheus, p. 80.

morally, not intellectually, deficient—indeed, an infidel).

5. Therefore, "that than which nothing greater can be conceived" exists in reality as well as in the mind.

There is no Step 6 where Anselm jumps to "this being is God" or Step 7 where he further jumps to "this being is the Christian God," and those are both huge leaps to make, particularly the last one. Thus, we can credit Anselm with formalizing the soft definition of the Christian God, born of their Platonist tradition, in which He is conceived vaguely as the greatest possible being. Anselm's reasoning, of course, is utterly errone-ous in more than one place. In fact, Richard Dawkins in *The God Delusion*, indicates that it is dicey to believe that the argument manages to "prove" the reality of God's existence in the universe without looking at a single piece of data from the world (instead, playing a game with words).[31] How can the argument be any-thing other than utterly fallacious, then?

Note the call to the book of Psalms. By using it, Anselm already implicitly assumes some things about there being a connection between "highest conceivable being" and the God in the Bible. He simply assumes, *a priori* and following Christian Neoplatonism, that the Bible is talking about the "ideal of idealness" god-concept. What if the God in the Bible cannot be seen as an extension of the philosopher's God? Maybe Christians have simply been wrong about this all

---

[31]   Dawkins, Richard (2006), *The God Delusion*, New York: Bantam, pp. 105-7.

along. Consider also the problem of coherence that arises from the omni properties that seem necessitated in any greatest-conceivable being. We can add another incoherence argument here. The ontological argument must fail because it requires a particular assumption that cannot have any grounding in reality: it is not even possible to conceive of a being greater than which nothing can exist because of the nature of the infinite, as I will explain.

There are a few possibilities that we should consider. One is that God has limited faculties; he exists devoid of omni properties. This avoids the problem of omni incoherence, although it also seems to contradict the premises of the ontological argument because one could easily imagine a being with at least one unlimited faculty. We are forced to reject either this position or the argument itself, then. To keep with the argument, it makes sense that the usual position on God assumes at least one infinite capacity (usually at least three, in fact: omnipotence, omniscience, and moral perfection, this last one accounting for several omnis in one). As soon as we assume one infinite capacity of God, though, that assumption leads us back to the question of "which infinity?" since we have infinitely many infinities to choose from that might represent the relevant quantity. This question, in terms of God's existence, is absolutely disastrous for Anselm's ontological argument.

Recall that given any infinity, we can create a larger infinity from it, yielding an infinite progression that cannot terminate. As soon as we assume one infinite size exists, we're immediately burdened with infinitely many larger than that as a consequence of the Zermelo-Fraenkel axioms that underlie modern mathematical thinking. Thus, even a being with any

178

specified amount of infinite ability or potency is the not highest since we can always conceive of more. In this case, the problem to the argument is insurmountable because it is impossible to conceive of a highest infinity—even in the mind—meaning that Step 4, and thus Step 5 (along with any subsequent jumps to a particular god), are invalid.

The proper conclusion to Anselm's ontological argument is a revised Step 4: *"It is impossible to conceive of a being 'than that which nothing greater can be conceived.'"* We must simply reject the primitive thinking exhibited in Psalms 14 as carrying any weight—yet again the scriptures are wrong. Simply calling God the "Most High" cannot solve the problem because no definitive concept of "most high" actually makes sense. It seems that infinite capacities of God are required for the ontological argument, and they are also another of its many deaths! *This* is why applying infinity to the God discussion is often seductive folly, and especially *this* is why applying even one infinite property to God fails.

The only potential escape here is to fall back on a purely qualitative understanding of the infinite. Combining Anselm's argument with Gödel's, for instance, could allow "Most High" to be defined as the accrual of every conceivable positive property with no negative properties. This, though, is the definition of the Platonic ideal of goodness—an abstraction. If believers want it that way, so be it, but we know that they do not.

Additionally, this argument also equivocates, now on the number of positive properties. Positive properties are also abstractly defined concepts, and so we have no reason to accept that there cannot be an infinite number of them, especially if the God that

179

they're supposed to define is an eternal God. Indeed, Gödel's first axiom states that any property entailed by a positive property is also a positive property. It quickly becomes easy to imagine, then, that each positive property creates a cascade of others. Indeed, I suspect it is the case that God defined in this way *must* exhibit an infinite number of positive properties, which has interesting consequences.

To present this, I will give three cases, though I expect any one of them would suffice on its own. Before starting, recall two of Gödel's statements. First, that the state of being "God-like" is that of possessing as essential properties all positive properties and no non-positive properties. Further, any property entailed by a positive property is also positive. Regardless of the definition of "positive" property we use here, omniscience and omnipotence are included beyond meaningful controversy.

Case 1 has us consider the statements "N is a prime number" for every natural number N. Each of these statements is unambiguously either true or false for every natural number N, of which most mathematicians agree there are an infinite number (finitists claim a *potential* infinite). For one specific, we know that every natural number that ends with a zero in our number system is *not* prime, returning potentially infinitely many known, immediately identifiable examples of numbers for which this statement is false. An omniscient being should know this answer for every one of these numbers, and as knowing each of those is entailed by omniscience, each is a positive property. Thus, there are infinitely many positive properties contained in being God-like.

Case 2 faces the situation in which an apologist might argue that an omniscient God need only know the answers to these questions for every natural number that non-omniscient beings will ever investigate. As discussed previously, apologists like William Lane Craig assert that there are only potential infinities at play above, in part because only finitely many numbers will ever be examined by any real mind.

Consider, then, the follow-up statements "N is a natural number that has been or will be examined on the question of being prime," for every natural number N. From the perspective of an omniscient deity, according to the above defense, this question will also have an unambiguous, known answer. Importantly, the truth value will be known for *every* natural number N by such an omniscient deity. Since knowing these truth values is entailed by omniscience, knowing each truth value is a positive property. Thus, there are infinitely many positive properties.

The potential objection here is that on strict finitism, or ultrafinitism, there simply aren't infinitely many natural numbers—the natural numbers only represent a *potential* infinity that can never be realized. This strikes me as a good rebuttal for temporal and local entities like ourselves, but it seems quite weak for an omniscient and eternal deity not limited in any worldly way. If most of what we call the natural numbers have no meaning, then surely an omniscient deity knows which of those numbers is largest. Yet if the deity knows which is largest, surely he can make sense of the square of that number, that number multiplied by itself, which has clear meaning as the number of unit squares composing a square with side of that largest meaningful length. Of course, this product is strictly larger than the one claimed to be largest (unless it is one, which is patently ridiculous).

Case 3 uses omnipotence and reminds us of Richard Carrier's *ex nihilo* discussion. Whether or not universes can pop into existence out of nothing, this property is guaranteed as a property of a deity identifiable with being the Creator. If some thing X is a positive, the property "able to create X" is also a positive property, but since God is omnipotent and able to create something from nothing, there can be no limitation on what God could create. For instance, there is no reason that God couldn't create another planet of sentient beings some vast distance away along with all of the potential for goodness and glory that might bring. Thus, there are infinitely many potential creations and hence infinitely many positive properties in being able to create each.

Admittedly, Case 3 isn't as powerful as Cases 1 and 2, but the only obvious way out of it is to claim that God made the universe in such a way that absolutely nothing else good can be done in it. Not only does this seem to contradict omnipotence, is also flies in the face of experience. At any rate, Cases 1 and 2 present a solid case that a deity defined to be "Most High" must exemplify an *actual infinity* of positive properties.

Therefore, if apologists like Craig want to take the tack that actual infinities exist only in the abstract, as I would, then since a divine being must exemplify an actual infinity of positive properties, such a divine being is itself necessarily abstract. On the other hand, if apologists like Craig wish to revise the claim that there are actual infinities present in the deity—making a case by special pleading for their increasingly abstruse God—then they face the fact that the existence of each infinity implies a larger infinity. This hand is no good for the apologist, though, because it undermines the meaningfulness of a "most high" being entirely, as we have seen. Curiously, then, given the situation, both "being infinite" and "not being infinite" seem to be positive properties for God, undermining Gödel's second axiom.

There is no winning here. God simply cannot be "Most High," neither finite nor infinite, neither quantitative nor qualitative. There is no such thing. Anselm's argument is only half-baked, due to a lack of solid understanding of imprecisely used concepts thrown about in a religious, and therefore inappropriate, context. Of course, if the ontological argument actually did succeed in getting off the ground, the believer should be besought by the fact that it applies equally well for Muslims to believe in Allah, for the cantankerous to believe in Irony the Equivocator,[32] and for any sort of divine being conceived as "most high." It would still require a substantial amount of ink (and hopefully, though doubtfully, no more blood) to attempt to justify one choice over another.

---

[32]   See *God Doesn't; We Do*, Chapter 4.

183

Dot, Dot, Dot

• • •
Conclusion
• • •

My conclusions are simple: infinity is easier to misuse than it is to use, mathematics is a human-made endeavor designed to help create a system by which we can better understand and communicate about reality, axiomatic systems ultimately only construct abstractions, and abstractions are not to be confused with reality. On this last point, because I think it is the most important take-home message given my subtitle, *Infinity Plus God Equals Folly*, it is incredibly important for us to examine our ideas—in part in order to recognize them as ideas, as the map, not the terrain. Theism reifies perfect goodness, an ideal that is inherently abstract and complex in meaning. Other points of view reify other ideals like liberty, justice, fairness, and even beingness, and theism has often been quick to bring those sorts of views within its fold. None of these ideas are real, though, in any sense other than as mental constructions by which we, thinking beings, attempt to understand the world. "God" is one such construction, and it's time we saw it more honestly.

The applications of the notion of infinity to discussions about God force the deity further out of the realm of the real, the natural, the physical, and into the realm of the abstract, the mental, the imaginary. This realm of abstractions also must be distinguished from the supernatural: the imaginary is not some other transcendent dimension and not an alternate reality. Hopefully this has been clearly exposed by seeing that the acceptance of the idea of infinity itself is defined by an axiom predicated upon a string of abstractions we use to make sense of quantities. Furthermore, the applications of infinity to the discussion are fraught with pitfalls and invitations to fall into error, even within the abstract world. Perhaps most important of these problems is highlighted in the last chapter in this collection: the widely accepted "Most High" notion of God from St. Anselm demands infinity and yet fails because of it because "most high," whether finite or infinite, is an inherently incoherent idea.

And "God" has to be infinite now. It cannot be finite and maintain theism—even if the Catholics revised their dogmas. Apologists aren't so crude about it, of course, instead opting to be slippery. Famous Christian apologist William Lane Craig explains it thusly, "'infinity' is just a sort of umbrella term used to cover all of God's superlative attributes." He wants to justify this statement by saying,

> [W]hen theologians speak of the infinity of God, they are not using the word in a mathematical sense to refer to an aggregate of an infinite number of elements. God's infinity is, as it were, qualitative, not quantitative. It means that God is metaphysically necessary, morally perfect, omnipotent, omniscient, eternal, and so on.[33]

What Craig reveals here is that theologians generally accept the idea that God is infinite in a number of

---

[33]   Craig, William Lane, "Is God Actually Infinite?", *Reasonable Faith with William Lane Craig*, http://www.reasonablefaith.org/is-god-actually-infinite#ixzz2bImoIQYR (retrieved August 15, 2013)

ways, and yet they do not want to handle the ramifications of that implication. They want it both ways.

Even Georg Cantor, the mathematician who opened the door to modern thinking about infinity, felt this way about God and infinity. Cantor wrote,

> The actual infinite arises in three contexts: first when it is realized in the most complete form, a fully independent and otherworldly being, *in Deo*, where I call it the Absolute Infinity or simply the Absolute; second when it occurs in the contingent, created world; third when the mind grasps it *in abstracto* as a mathematical magnitude, number, or order type.[34]

Before taking this as a crack in my argument, though, observe that Cantor lacked the perspective of the developments his work produced. For instance, he spoke without knowing how the Zermelo-Fraenkel axioms of set theory would reinvent how we think about mathematics—indeed we call the older approach "naive set theory" now. Indeed, Zermelo's set theory puts restrictions on how we conceive of sets in a way that essentially discounts Cantor's first context (without mentioning the bad metaphor called "God"), and Cantor's second context is a very suspect notion (that William Lane Craig argues is not logically possible, incidentally). Cantor's third context, the one that remains, is exactly the argument I make.

Furthermore, the reason Cantor's first context fails is the same reason there can be no "Most High" God mentioned in Chapter 16—any attempt to name a Most

---

[34]   As quoted in Rucker, Rudy (1987), *Mind Tools: The Five Levels of Mathematical Reality*, Boston: Houghton Mifflin.

High immediately admits something higher. Thus, an apologist trying to use Cantor's statement is basically appealing to an outdated mode of thought that, when modernized, leads exactly to the case I am making.

And yet these theologians, alleged to be at the height of philosophical theism, are explicitly admitting that "infinite" is an idea necessary to discuss God. Even Cantor believed it, although he was a staunchly religious man who felt that the orthodox relationship of God and mathematics should be preserved.[35] For some centuries now, theologians have implied that infinity is intrinsic to God, and we should wonder why.

The answer isn't so hard: because it has to be. When "God" was conceived, at least in the Abrahamic traditions, he lived on a mountaintop. When people climbed the mountain, God wasn't there to be met, and when they descended the other side to meet new people, they were forced to place God in the sky and make God big enough for both peoples. We've been to the sky; in fact we've been above it. God isn't there either. He did not meet us in low earth orbit; he did not meet us when we walked upon the moon; and our robots have not found him on any planet in our solar system or, now, just outside it. Our telescopes cannot see him, even as they peer out into the apparently edgeless universe, and so people have moved God beyond the universe to an imaginary realm, and as God went, they've had to make him big enough to account for it all.

---

[35]   Dauben, Joseph W. (1979), *Georg Cantor: His Mathematics and Philosophy of the Infinite*, Boston: Harvard University Press, p. 295.

Within that "all" is not only every conception of God that humans have entertained and worshiped, but also every potential notion of God that is conceivable. Monotheism demands it, in lieu of an actual physical God of this world. The potential conceptions of God are infinite, and so God too must be infinite to usurp them all. But as we've seen, God cannot be infinite, unless believers would also accept he must also be abstract— that is, mental stuff. Though apologists may defend this idea of God, a majority of believers do not accept an unreal philosophical deity of this kind. Theirs is a living, breathing, acting agent who will one day judge the living and the dead, and this is a fact too easy to lose sight of when talking with apologists.

Of course, the believers don't care much either. They are content to have plausible-sounding theological arguments that provide the appearance of an intellectual shield that protects their nonsense beliefs. With a bar set so low, apologists merely have to continue arguing for how some concept of God, or properties ascribed to it, *could* make sense, yet again in the abstract. If that includes making their God into a Platonic ideal, via the infinite or any number of other "mysteries," it hardly stops them. An abstract ideal isn't what their audience hears anyway.

All of this exalted nonsense makes sense only if we view it as a gradual and reluctant acceptance of the fact of the matter: God is an abstraction, a collection of mental models via which people interpret the world. These tools, unfortunately all called by one name, make for relatively poor maps of reality, though, because while we imagine that "God" appears to tell us this or that about the world, we're left with no workable answers, no useful predictions, and much disagreement and confusion.

189

Worse, these maps don't all match each other, despite the unity in name, which leads to conflict as irreconcilable attempts to understand reality clash with each other, lacking a methodology anchored in reality. These conflicts have been, are, and will continue to be bloody and horrible. Now that we have better methods for understanding our world—the scientific methodologies being key among those—these conflicts must also be seen as profoundly tragic. We must discard these old, misleading maps, then, and we should stop confusing them for the terrain.

Suggested Reading

Many of the topics in this book were introduced without thorough background, and others are covered only lightly. Here is a short list of some suggested reading for those seeking more information.

The following entries in The Stanford Encyclopedia of Philosophy (http://plato.stanford.edu) are highly recommended very useful primers on many of these topics:

- ⚔ Bayesian Epistemology
- ⚔ Continuity and Infinitesimals
- ⚔ Continuum Hypothesis
- ⚔ Fictionalism in the Philosophy of Mathematics
- ⚔ Formalism in the Philosophy of Mathematics
- ⚔ Fuzzy Logic
- ⚔ Interpretations of Probability
- ⚔ Intuitionism in the Philosophy of Mathematics
- ⚔ Logicism and Neologicism
- ⚔ Modal Logic
- ⚔ Philosophy of Mathematics
- ⚔ Platonism in the Philosophy of Mathematics
- ⚔ Properties
- ⚔ Russell's Paradox
- ⚔ Set Theory: Constructive and Intuitionistic ZF
- ⚔ Supertasks
- ⚔ The Axiom of Choice
- ⚔ Zeno's Paradoxes
- ⚔ Zermelo's Axiomatization of Set Theory

Similarly, the majority of the entries in *Wikipedia* on the mathematical and philosophical topics covered here are quite good. More usefully, they are typically well-referenced, providing more opportunities for deeper study.

For more information about finitism/ultrafinite mathematics, including this reference to Mycielski's Finitary Theorem, see Lavine, Shaughan, *Understanding the Infinite*, (Boston: Harvard University Press, 1994). To be clear, I have only skimmed this work other than a few relevant points, and I should note that the mathematics involved is quite rigorous and may be inaccessible to lay readers.

For a very accessible introduction to the bizarreness of the mathematics surrounding infinity and a short introduction to probability (among other topics), consider the following textbook: Ed Burger and Michael Starbird, *The Heart of Mathematics: An Invitation to Effective Thinking*, 2nd ed., Emeryville, CA: Key College Publishing, 2005. This book is written for incoming college students who do not intend to study math, and it assumes little more than very basic algebra and arithmetic to work through it.

More mathematically sophisticated readers who are interested in understanding modern analysis, including its applications to measure theory, are encouraged to check out two books by Walter Rudin. First, *Principles of Mathematical Analysis*, and second, *Real and Complex Analysis*, 3rd edition. Both are part of the *International Series in Pure and Applied Mathematics*. These are pitched at the senior undergraduate and beginning postgraduate level in mathematics and are quite difficult (and will be inaccessible to lay readers).

To better understand how to apply Bayesian methods to hypothesis evaluation, consider Elliott Sober's treatment in his *Evidence and Evolution: The Logic Behind Science*, Cambridge University Press (2008).

Ian Hacking's *An Introduction to Probability and Inductive Logic*, Cabridge University Press (2001) is a great resource and is intended for beginners and non-specialists.

A far more technical introduction can be had in A.J. Ayer: *Probability and Evidence*, Columbia University Press (2005). This book is much more technical than Hacking's.

Dot, Dot, Dot

Glossary of mathematical terms:

As the mathematical terminology is likely to be over-whelming at times for a lay reader, I am including a plain-language (read: non-technical!) glossary of the mathematical terms I employ throughout this book. Mathematicians will forgive the intentional lack of technical precision here, I trust.

Almost Surely: Formally, "almost sure" (or "almost certain") means true off a set with probability-measure equal to zero. Loosely, this means that the total amount of contradictory information is negligible in that it contributes no weight.

Axiom: An axiom is a statement or proposition taken to be self-evidently true and presupposed in order to build logical frameworks.

Axiom of Choice: The axiom of choice states that given an infinite collection of sets of indistinguishable objects, each containing at least one thing, it is possible to create a new set by choosing exactly one thing from each set in the collection.

Axiom of Infinity: The axiom of infinity states, essentially, that at least one infinite set exists (abstractly).

Axiomatic System: An axiomatic system is a collection of propositions, each paired with a truth value, where the truth value of each proposition is determined by the kind of logic employed upon the axioms presupposed for the system.

Bayesianism (Philosophy of Probability): Also known as *subjectivism*, Bayesianism espouses an epistemic understanding of probabilities. The basic methodology is to assign a prior probability (or plausibility) to an event or hypothesis (inherently subjectively) and then to update that guess by repeated applications of Bayes's Theorem, which weighs evidence (often also subjectively) to give an estimated updated probability known as the posterior probability. After each application of the theorem, the former posterior probability can be used as a new prior probability when more evidence is collected. Bayesians understand probability in terms of our degree of confidence in whether hypotheses are true.

Cardinality: Cardinality is a generalized notion of the answer to the question "how many?" More specifically, the cardinality of a set is the property shared in common between all sets whose elements can be matched up in a one-to-one correspondence (without leaving out of the matching any from either set). It generalizes "how many?" by allowing infinite answers to the question, when applicable.

Continuous: Not discrete. (See **discrete**.) A good example is the real number line, which has no holes or gaps of any kind between its elements. Importantly, continuous sets cannot be put into one-to-one correspondence with any set that is discrete.

Continuum Hypothesis: The statement that there is no set whose cardinality is strictly between the cardinality of the natural numbers and that of the real line (continuum). A common generalization of the continuum hypothesis posits that the sizes of infinity are discrete. The Zermelo-Fraenkel Axioms together with the generalized continuum hypothesis imply the axiom of choice, yielding ZFC.

Countable Additivity: The property that when adding together *countably* infinitely many values or fewer, addition works as it normally does. The key thing to note is that this property does not apply to sums of *uncountably* many values.

Countable Infinity: The cardinality of the set of natural numbers, {1,2,3,...}. Somewhat ironically named.

Discrete: Data or sets whose values are individually separate and distinct are called discrete. The natural numbers and every finite set are discrete. Indeed, discrete formally means finite or countable in cardinality.

Exponentiation: The operation of raising one value to the power of another. With infinite sets, this requires some care, but to be brief, the infinite cardinality is the exponent.

Fictionalism (Philosophy of Mathematics): The widely rejected position that abstract mathematical entities are "useful fictions" that do not exist in reality.

Finite: Only having a limited quantity of elements. Not infinite. (See **infinite**.)

Finite Additivity: The property that only when adding together finitely many values can we be assured that addition works as it normally does. Particularly, countable additivity may, but need not, hold.

Frequentism (Philosophy of Probability): The position that interprets the meaning of probability of an event as the proportion of successes against total trials in a large number of repeated, identical experiments testing for the event.

Formalism (Mathematical Philosophy): Very briefly, formalism holds that mathematical objects and operations are formal abstract constructions and nothing more.

Googol: Ten to the one-hundredth power, that is a one followed by one hundred zeroes. Not a very big number but more than the number of atoms in the observable universe by about ten million trillion times over. Because I almost never see it written out, this is a googol written out in our usual notation.
10,000,000,000,000,000,000,000,000,000,000,00
0,000,000,000,000,000,000,000,000,000,000,000
,000,000,000,000,000,000,000,000,000.

Googolplex: Ten to the googol power, that is a one followed by a googol zeroes. Not a very big number, but in light of the observation in the definition for googol, the googolplex is a number too large to write out via our usual system even if a single atom could represent each zero.

Hilbert's Hotel: A famous analogy crafted by mathematician David Hilbert and used to expose the non-intuitiveness of infinite cardinals and correspondences between countable sets. Hilbert imagines a hotel with infinitely many rooms and performs several thought-experiments with the construction.

Infinite/Infinity: A set is said to be infinite if an element can be removed from it without changing its cardinality. Loosely, this word is meant to mean "without bound" in a quantitative sense. Infinity is the noun representing this idea.

Infinitesimal: A value infinitely small, the reciprocal of some infinite cardinality ($1/\infty$), or a hypothetical value larger than zero but smaller than every positive value. It stands to reason that infinitesimals are smaller when the cardinality of infinity determining them is larger.

Infinite Monkey Theorem: This theorem states that given infinitely many random trials, every possible occurrence with nonzero probability will almost surely occur eventually (indeed, thus necessarily infinitely many times). "Eventually" may take a *lot* of trials.

Intuitionism (Mathematical Philosophy): Intuition-ists hold the philosophical view that mathematics is nothing but a creation of the human mind and that with no minds to think it, mathematics would not exist.

Irrational Numbers: Numbers that cannot be written as a fraction of integers.

Law of Large Numbers: The law of large numbers is a mathematical theorem (actually, a few of them in various strengths) that states that as the number of repeated identical trials for a random event increases to very large numbers, the frequency of successes approaches the theoretical propensity of that event's occurrence. If one could complete infinitely many trials, the result states that the frequency would equal the propensity, almost surely. This theorem provides a connection between the frequentist and propensitist interpretations of probability theory, when it applies.

Limit Cardinal: A cardinal is a limit cardinal if it cannot be obtained from a smaller cardinal by repeated applications of succession (addition). Every infinite cardinal is a limit cardinal, and no finite cardinal is a limit cardinal.

Logic: Loosely, a logic is a rule that assigns values, called truth values, to propositions following a collection of axioms in an axiomatic system. We are most familiar with "Boolean" logic, which assigns only *true* and *false* as truth values, but there are logics with three, four, more, and even infinitely many truth values.

Measure: A measure is a systematic way to assign a numerical value to the subsets of a set, intuitively understood as a size. Measures can be thought of as a way to generalize lengths of intervals on the real number line. This standard generalization of lengths of intervals on the real number line is called *Lebesgue measure* after the father of measure theory, Henri Lebesgue.

Modal Logic: A system of formal logic developed in the 1960s to extend usual (propositional and predicate) logic to handle "modalities," which are qualifiers of statements, most notably "necessarily" and "possibly."

Natural Numbers: The set of all positive integers, {1,2,3,...}. These are sometimes called "counting numbers," a term that is also sometimes meant to include zero. Some branches of mathematics, for this reason, call the set {0,1,2,...} the set of natural numbers.

Natural Density: The natural density of a subset of the natural numbers is the value determined by a method that assigns the proportion of the natural numbers that subset intuitively represents. For example, the set of even natural numbers {2,4,6,...} has natural density one-half. The natural density can be determined, when applicable, by examining the sequence of densities one step at a time. Specifically, each value in the sequence is the fraction with bottom number the position in the sequence and top number the number of elements in the set up to and including that value. For example, using the even natural numbers, we get a sequence of densities that approach one half as ever more of the natural numbers are considered with sequence (0/1, 1/2, 1/3, 2/4, 2/5, 3/6, ...). Every other number is one-half, and the ones between approach one-half asymptotically from below. The natural density of every finite subset of the natural numbers is zero.

Number: A number is a mathematical object used to count, label, and measure. This definition is included to highlight the term "mathematical object," which gives it the abstract feel I am trying to convey.

Peano Axioms of Number Theory: A set of axioms originally devised by nineteenth-century mathematician Giuseppe Peano for the purpose of formalizing the natural numbers.

Platonism (Mathematical Philosophy): Platonism is the philosophical point of view that mathematical objects have a form of perfect and abstract existence in a realm of ideas. This idea is often taken more broadly to imply that our mathematical objects and scientific models represent the true nature of reality. Key to this philosophy is that this realm exists *independently of minds* and truths about them are *discovered* by thinking minds.

Plausibility: In this context, plausibility means nearly the same thing as probability but as applied to hypotheses from a Bayesian perspective. Here, we interpret the probability of validity of the hypothesis as a statement of our degree of knowledge that it is valid. (See **probability**.)

Probability: A measure of estimation of how likely it is that something will happen or that a proposition is true (see also **plausibility**). Probabilities always have a value between zero (0%), indicating impossibility, and one (100%), indicating certainty.

Probability Density Function (PDF): A function (rule) that describes how likely it is for a random variable to take on each possible given value.

Probability Measure: A probability measure is a measure on a space with total measure one. (See **measure**.)

Propensitism (Philosophy of Probability): Propensitists interpret probability as a physical propensity, or disposition, or tendency of a given physical situation to yield an outcome of a certain kind or to produce a long-run relative frequency of such an outcome. In brief, they conceive of probability objectively as dependent upon "chance."

Real Number/Real Line: A real number is any number that can (potentially) be written in decimal expansion form, and the real number line, also called the "continuum," is a one-dimensional geometric representation of the set of real numbers. The real numbers are somewhat ironically named.

Russell's Paradox: A paradox, identified by Bertrand Russell, in set theory that arises by asking if the set of all sets (that do not contain themselves) can exist. It is a paradox because the set of all sets is itself a set, but it cannot contain itself. The resolution of this paradox totally revamped set theory.

Set/Subset: Very loosely, a set is a collection of objects, real or abstract. A subset of a set is a set comprised only of elements from the parent set. There are very tricky details here that are outside of the scope of this text. Readers are encouraged to investigate more if interested.

Set Theory: The branch of mathematical logic that studies sets.

Skewes' (and Graham's) Numbers: Skewes' "number" is any of the extremely large numbers used by the mathematician Stanley Skewes as upper bounds in a difficult mathematical proof. Skewes' numbers are so large that they are difficult to write down in any notation that can easily interpreted. The larger is ten to the power of (ten to the power of (ten to the power of 963)). This number dwarfs ten to the googolplex power, but it is very small in the grand scheme of things. Indeed, it is much smaller than the also very small Graham's number, also an upper bound for a proof. Graham's number is so large that it cannot even be succinctly written in exponential notation and required the invention of an entirely new notation to express it. Still, that notation proves essentially worthless for the task. Graham's number is defined recursively in 64 steps, and even the first step is utterly intractable. I gave up trying to determine the number of digits of the result of the first step after several hours of getting nowhere. The second step requires doing the same thing as in the first step but the first step number of times, where as the number of repetitions in the first step is four. Each step proceeds the same way, using the result of the previous step to determine the number of repetitions. Incidentally, though, the last ten digits of Graham's number are known to be ...2464195387. Again, like all the rest of them, it too is much, much smaller than most natural numbers.

Strong Limit Cardinal: A cardinal is a strong limit cardinal if it cannot be obtained by successorship (addition), i.e. is a limit cardinal, and cannot be obtained by exponentiation. Unless we get into some fringe hyper-large cardinal explorations, countable infinity is the only strong limit cardinal, separating finite and infinite cardinalities.

Successor: The successor to a natural number is the next natural number, as five is to four. The successor function is the function that adds one (to the previous value).

Surreal Numbers: An arithmetic continuum containing the real numbers, infinite numbers, and infinitesimal numbers. They were introduced by John H. Conway.

Ultrafinitism: In the philosophy of mathematics, this is the position that denies the axiom of infinity on the grounds that no infinite set can ever be completed.

Uncountable Infinity: Every infinite cardinality larger than the natural numbers is uncountable. For example, the cardinality of the real numbers is uncountable. The members of sets of these cardinalities cannot be written in a complete list because any such list will necessarily leave off most of the members.

Zermelo-Fraenkel Axioms of Set Theory: A set of axioms proposed in the early twentieth century to define set theory while avoiding the paradoxes raised by a less careful formulation of set theory. The axiom of infinity is one of those included here.

ZFC (ZF with Choice), cf. ZF~C: ZFC is the axiomatic system of set theory composed of the Zermelo-Fraenkel axioms plus the axiom of choice. It is the most commonly used axiomatic system among mathematicians at present. ZF~C is the system composed of the Zermelo-Fraenkel axioms with the negation of the axiom of choice. Note that both of these systems contain one more axiom than ZF alone.

Dot, Dot, Dot

Bibliography and Works Cited

A.J. Ayer, *Probability and Evidence, Columbia University Press, 2005.*

Balaguer, Mark, "Fictionalism in the Philosophy of Mathematics," *The Stanford Encyclopedia of Philosophy* (Fall 2013 Edition), Edward N. Zalta (ed.).

Bell, John L., "The Axiom of Choice," *The Stanford Encyclopedia of Philosophy* (Winter 2012 Edition), Edward N. Zalta (ed.).

Burger, Ed, and Michael Starbird, *The Heart of Mathematics: An Invitation to Effective Thinking*, 2nd ed., Emeryville, CA: Key College Publishing, 2005.

Carrier, Richard (2012), *"Ex Nihilo Onus Merdae Fit,"* Richard Carrier Blogs, http://freethoughtblogs.com/carrier/ archives/468 (retrieved August 7, 2013).

Carrier, Richard, "Naturalism is True, Theism is Not: Carrier's Opening Statement", Carrier-Wanchick Debate, *The Secular Web*, 2006, http://www.infidels.org/library/modern/richard_ carrier/carrier-wanchick/carrier1.html (retrieved August 15, 2013).

Carrier, Richard, *Proving History: Bayes's Theorem and the Quest for a Historical Jesus*, Amherst, NY: Prometheus, 2012.

Carroll, Lewis. *Alice's Adventures in Wonderland*, originally published in 1865.

Craig, William Lane, "Counting Down from Infinity," *Reasonable Faith with William Lane Craig*, http://www.reasonablefaith. org/counting-down-from-infinity (accessed 18 Sept. 2013).

Craig, William Lane, "Does God Know an Actually Infinite Number of Things?" *Reasonable Faith with William Lane Craig*, http://www.reasonablefaith.org/does-god-know-an-actually-infinite-number-of-things (accessed 18 Sept. 2013).

Craig, William Lane, "Forming an Actual Infinite by Successive Addition," *Reasonable Faith with William Lane Craig*, http://www.reasonablefaith.org/forming-an-actual-infinite-by-successive-addition (accessed 18 Sept. 2013).

Craig, William Lane, "God and Infinity," *Reasonable Faith with William Lane Craig* http://www.reasonablefaith.org/god-and-infinity (accessed 18 Sept. 2013).

Craig, William Lane, "God, Time, and Creation," *Reasonable Faith with William Lane Craig*, http://www.reasonablefaith. org/god-time-and-creation (accessed 18 Sept., 2013).

Craig, William Lane, "Is God Actually Infinite?" *Reasonable Faith with William Lane Craig*, http://www.reasonablefaith. org/is-god-actually-infinite#ixzz2bImoIQYR (retrieved August 15, 2013)

Craig, William Lane, *The Kalām Cosmological Argument*, Eugene, Oregon: Wipf and Stock, 2000.

Dauben, Joseph W., *Georg Cantor: His Mathematics and Philosophy of the Infinite*, Boston: Harvard University Press, 1979.

Dawkins, Richard, *The God Delusion*, New York: Bantam, 2006.

Descartes, René, *Meditations on First Philosophy, with Selections from the Objections and Replies (Cambridge Texts in the History of Philosophy)*, Ed. John Cottingham, Cambridge University Press, 1996.

Dupré, Maurice, and Frank Tipler, "New Axioms for Rigorous Bayesian Probability," *Bayesian Analysis* (2009) **4**, Number 3, pp. 599-606.

Hacking, Ian, *An Introduction to Probability and Inductive Logic*, Cambridge University Press, 2001.

Hájek, Alan, "Interpretations of Probability," *The Stanford Encyclopedia of Philosophy* (Winter 2012 Edition), Edward N. Zalta (ed.).

Hajek, Petr, "Fuzzy Logic," *The Stanford Encyclopedia of Philosophy* (Fall 2010 Edition), Edward N. Zalta (ed.).

Hallett, Michael, "Zermelo's Axiomatization of Set Theory," *The Stanford Encyclopedia of Philosophy* (Fall 2013 Edition), Edward N. Zalta (ed.).

Horsten, Leon, "Philosophy of Mathematics," *The Stanford Encyclopedia of Philosophy* (Summer 2012 Edition), Edward N. Zalta (ed.).

Iemhoff, Rosalie, "Intuitionism in the Philosophy of Mathematics," *The Stanford Encyclopedia of Philosophy* (Fall 2013 Edition), Edward N. Zalta (ed.).

Koellner, Peter, "The Continuum Hypothesis," *The Stanford Encyclopedia of Philosophy* (Summer 2013 Edition), Edward N. Zalta (ed.).

Krauss, Lawrence, *A Universe From Nothing: Why There is Something Rather than Nothing*, New York: Atria Books, 2013.

Laraudogoitia, Jon Pérez, "Supertasks," *The Stanford Encyclopedia of Philosophy* (Fall 2013 Edition), Edward N. Zalta (ed.).

Lavine, Shaughan, *Understanding the Infinite*, Boston: Harvard University Press, 1994.

Lindsay, James A., *God Doesn't; We Do: Only Humans Can Solve Human Challenges*, CreateSpace, 2012.

Linnebo, Øystein, "Platonism in the Philosophy of Mathematics," *The Stanford Encyclopedia of Philosophy* (Fall 2011 Edition), Edward N. Zalta (ed.).

Loftus, John W., *Why I Became an Atheist: A Former Preacher Rejects Christianity*, Amherst: Prometheus, 2008.

Lowder, Jeffery Jay, "The Evidential Argument from the History of Science (AHS), *The Secular Outpost*, http://www.patheos. com/blogs/secularoutpost/2012/06/16/the-evidential-argument-from-the-history-of-science-ahs/ (retrieved August 15, 2013).

"Richard Dawkins on Bill Maher," Online video clip, *YouTube*. YouTube, 11 Apr. 2008. accessed 18 Sept. 2013.

Rucker, Rudy, *Mind Tools: The Five Levels of Mathematical Reality*, Boston: Houghton Mifflin, 1987.

Silberman, Steve, "Life After Darth," *Wired*, May 2005.

Sober, Elliott, *Evidence and Evolution: The Logic Behind Science*, Cambridge University Press, 2008.

Stewart, Ian, *Letters to a Young Mathematician (Art of Mentoring)*, New York: Basic Books, 2006.

Swoyer, Chris and Frcancesco Orilia, "Properties," *The Stanford Encyclopedia of Philosophy* (Winter 2011 Edition), Edward N. Zalta (ed.).

Unwin, Stephen D., *The Probability of God: A Simple Calculation That Proves the Ultimate Truth*, New York: Three Rivers Press, 2004.

Weir, Alan, "Formalism in the Philosophy of Mathematics," *The Stanford Encyclopedia of Philosophy* (Fall 2011 Edition), Edward N. Zalta (ed.).

Zimmerman, Otto. "Infinity." *The Catholic Encyclopedia*. Vol. 8. New York: Robert Appleton Company, 1910. http://www.newadvent.org/cathen/08004a.htm (Accessed 18 Sept. 2013).

Dot, Dot, Dot